The natural history of
Upper Teesdale

© Margaret Till

Edited by
Steve Gater
(for Durham Wildlife Trust)

5th edition

Visitor information

Most of the land in Upper Teesdale belongs to the Raby Estate or to the Strathmore Estate. The Dale lies within the North Pennines Area of Outstanding National Beauty (NPAONB) and 8,800 hectares forms the Moor House–Upper Teesdale National Nature Reserve. Many areas are covered by specific designations to protect and conserve them.

See the NPAONB site:
http://www.explorenorthpennines.org.uk
for visitor information. Please recognise and respect the fact that the countryside is a farmer's home and workshop and that all land belongs to someone, even if you have a right of access. Follow all guidance provided, including the Country Code and codes for specific activities, including water sports. Please give generously to the local economy.

Fifth edition published in the United Kingdon in 2018 by Mosaic (Teesdale) Ltd, Snaisgill, Middleton-in-Teesdale DL12 0RP

LOTTERY FUNDED

ISBN 978 0 9935970 8 4

Design, layout and typesetting by
Mosaic Design and Print, Middleton-in-Teesdale DL12 0RP

FROM TEES TO TYNE

This book is part of the wider 'The natural history of Upper Teesdale' project that is generously supported by **The Heritage Lottery Fund**, to whom much appreciation is offered.

Durham Wildlife Trust is a registered charity (N° 501038)

Cover images: main image River Tees and Widdybank; back cover River Tees in Autumn, Bird's-eye primrose, Cauldron Snout and Swaledale Sheep at Langdon Beck Show. All images © Steve Gater.

Contents

The authors

The authors may be contacted via Durham Wildlife Trust (tel. 0191 5843112, www.durhamwt.com) or directly if shown below.

Lord Barnard DL, Raby Estates

Margaret E Bradshaw, MBE, PhD: retired lecturer, University of Durham

John C Coulson, PhD, DSc: retired Reader in Animal Ecology, University of Durham

Trevor Crisp PhD, deceased: formerly research scientist, Moor House National Nature Reserve

David A J Evans: Professor in the Department of Geography, University of Durham (d.j.a.evans@durham.ac.uk)

Ian Findlay, MBE: retired warden, local farmer and wildlife enthusiast

Tom Gledhill: Heritage at Risk Officer, Historic England North East

Martyn G Kelly, PhD: environmental consultant specialising in the ecology of freshwater algae (www.microscopesandmonsters.wordpress.com, MGKelly@bowburn-consultancy.co.uk)

Ben Lamb: manager of the Tees River Trust (tel. 01325 787651, http://teesriverstrust.org)

Stephen Trotter: freelance consultant, formerly Director (England and Living Landscapes), Royal Society of Wildlife Trusts

Judith Turner, PhD: retired lecturer, University of Durham

Brian Whitton: Emeritus Professor of Botany, University of Durham

Brian Young: Honorary Research Fellow, Department of Earth Sciences, University of Durham: (brian.young@hotmail.co.uk)

Foreword

Lord Barnard

My interest in Upper Teesdale stems from my late father who, through his stewardship of Raby Estates, had a great affection for the landscape and rugged unspoilt qualities of the area, and in particular for the farming community of the upper Dale. I was brought up east of Barnard Castle, in a countryside of arable crops on rich soil and moderate rainfall. On sunny summers' days we would call up a hill farmer to find out what the weather was doing 'up the Dale'. More often than not an extra jumper and raincoat were required. If good, there was nowhere better and we would set off for an afternoon of paddling in the becks, picnics and walks. Although less than thirty minutes' drive from home it felt like a different world.

As a child you tend to take everything for granted and so it was with Upper Teesdale. The prolific bird life, the wild flowers, the rock formations and drama of the River Tees itself seemed normal. It was only after visiting other upland areas that there was the realisation that Upper Teesdale was different, even unique. Where else could one find the mix of the black grouse leks, the cries of curlews and peewits, the spring gentians, the hay meadows rich in wild flowers, and the small neat white-washed farms dotted over the landscape?

We are blessed to have an area such as Upper Teesdale on our doorstep, and in particular its botanical interest that is of such national and international significance. We are also fortunate to have the benefit of the specialist and authoritative knowledge, in some cases gained over a lifetime in the area, that the contributors bring to this edition of the Natural History of Upper Teesdale. It will be an invaluable resource to both layman and specialist to further their understanding of this remarkable area. It is only by understanding what we have that the right decisions can be made in the care and future management of the unique and complex environment that makes up Upper Teesdale.

Introduction

The Editor

This edition (the first was published in 1965) marks continuing interest in the outstanding beauty of Upper Teesdale. It aims to inform, inspire and engage people who live, learn or work in the area and visitors from near or far. Chapters are written by contributors, with key local knowledge, who are experts in their field. Each is a separate, authoritative explanation and celebration of the Dale and suggests that there is still more to learn about what we see today.

Rightly, Upper Teesdale inspired poets and artists, inaugurated early-Victorian tourism and has been the subject of much scientific enquiry. People love the Dale. The landscape, physical and living, is unique in many ways. But different pressures threaten the Dale's economy, culture, landform, habitats and wildlife. Change is inevitable, that's what happens in nature. But human decisions and actions will shape the type and extent of change. If we want our children, and future generations, to enjoy Upper Teesdale as we do today, their best interests should be at the heart of development and future conservation strategy. We have a choice.

As Margaret Bradshaw wrote in 2003, 'I have a hope that the Dale will still support the largest number of rare plants in a limited space in Britain after I am gone. For we hold in trust the nation's oldest Heritage in the Dale'. Let Upper Teesdale benefit from development and conservation that are informed, enlightened, joined-up and that support a living Dale.

Acknowledgements

The publication of this book and wider Natural History of Upper Teesdale project involving training, talks, guided walks and work with local schools, has been made possible by generous funding from **The Heritage Lottery Fund**, to whom much appreciation is offered. The project aims to give something valuable back to the many people who buy lottery tickets. Thank you.

The authors of this book, and previous editions, have freely provided time and expertise to research, write and support the project. Their writing has been informed by views of knowledgeable local residents and others. Thank you to all. Credit is given against all illustrations and images in the book — thank you to everyone for your expertise. Thank you to Judith Mashiter of Mosaic Teesdale Ltd for her enthusiasm, expertise and patience. Many others have also helped in various ways. Thank you all for your kindness. Finally, thank you for reading this edition and enjoy learning more about this wonderful Dale.

Chapter 1

People

Tom Gledhill

'Some six or seven thousand years ago a family of Stone Age people camped for the summer on a small level area of grassland just below the limestone escarpment of Middle Hurth Edge high on the hills between Ettersgill and Langdon Beck. They could look out southward over the heavily forested valley of the Tees to Cronkley Fell while to east and west lay an expanse of open woodland. Behind their campsite was a cave in the limestone from which a small stream issued. These people were hunters and gatherers: hunting deer and wild cattle, fishing, collecting eggs and various plant foods. Though most of their toolkit of flint and chert had been made elsewhere new tools had to be made or re-sharpened and broken and worn out ones replaced. The debris from this together with lost or discarded tools – scrapers, knives and arrowheads – was scattered around the camp.

About three thousand years later the former campsite was re-used by people who constructed a long low mound of earth and stones. We do not know the purpose of this but in building it many of the flints abandoned by the previous occupiers became included in the mound. Later still, just over two thousand years ago another group of people who were farming the area – even growing oats- used this mound as a place to bury beneath small stone cairns the cremated remains of some of their number.

In another five hundred years there was a further development when a bank of earth and boulders was built over the mound enclosing a circular area which apparently had no entrance. The cairns were disturbed and only one was left intact covered by the soil of the enclosure bank. The enclosure and its bank may have had some religious purpose. During all this time the cave in the limestone cliff had been used by wild animals and also at some unknown date for some human burial.

About two hundred years ago these uplands from which the trees had long since disappeared were enclosed into fields by the long straight stone walls which are such a familiar feature of the landscape today.

From 1878 to 1885 the cave was excavated by members of the Backhouse family of York and Darlington. Large quantities of animal bone and some human remains were discovered and deposited in the Yorkshire Museum. At the same time quarrying was going on at the site, a limekiln was in operation and eventually the cave was almost completely destroyed leaving only a tiny area to be excavated in 1969 -70 by Mr C Simms.

The latest activity at Middle Hurth was the excavation carried out by Dr K. Fairless and the author in 1978-79 and it is from this work that much of the information above has been derived.'

The brief account above was written by the late Dennis Coggins as the introduction to his chapter on the people of Upper Teesdale in the 2003 edition of this book. He and his friend Dr Ken Fairless remain the most significant contributors to our knowledge of the history and archaeology of Upper Teesdale. Much of what Dennis wrote in 2003 is still relevant and provides an evocative account of one small part of Teesdale. Since Dennis's account there have been some significant contributions to our understanding of Man's role in the development of the landscape of Upper Teesdale, and our knowledge of the rest of the North Pennines has been nothing short of revolutionised.

Dennis's story starts with Mesolithic hunter gatherers who followed the ice sheet north as it retreated at the end of the last ice age some 12,000 years ago. These small bands of people were part of the North Pennine landscape for the next five and a half thousand years. They saw huge changes as the bare postglacial landscape was colonised first by arctic / alpine vegetation, dwarf shrubs, birch and juniper, later becoming dominated by pine woodland, which in turn gave way to a largely deciduous woodland cover.

Mesolithic hunter gatherers travelled widely using different parts of the landscape at different times of year. Evidence of their presence is widespread, particularly as scatters of flint such as that described by Dennis in the introduction, or the site discovered by Dennis at Stable Crag on the Tees near Wynch Bridge where we can imagine people exploiting the narrowing in the river to catch or spear migrating salmon. Like hunter gatherers the world over these people would have known their environment intimately, exploiting an incredible variety of plants and animals for food, medicine, tools and shelter. There is evidence, particularly from the study of peat cores, that these ancestors of ours actively manipulated the landscape, making small temporary clearings to attract grazing animals and encourage crops of hazel nuts.

The first farmers reached Britain about six and a half thousand years ago, just after the land bridge which had connected Britain to the continent was finally covered by the North Sea. It isn't clear how big a presence these first farmers had in Upper Teesdale, but there are intriguing hints of their presence including the long stone mound described by Dennis in his introduction, and at Blackmea Crag Sike above Holwick Scar, again described by Dennis, which consists of two or three small enclosures (fields?) and possibly a rectangular building. Overlying these is a large mound of burnt stones. These mounds of burnt stones, referred to as burnt mounds, now seem to be one of the most common visible remains left by Bronze Age settlers throughout the North Pennines. When excavated, these mounds of burnt and cracked stones incorporate several hearths and a trough, and like the example at Blackmea Crag Sike are located close to water, often streams or springs. They are often interpreted as saunas, and we may imagine Bronze Age farmers indulging in ritual cleansing like some North American Indians in the nineteenth century, before going on hunting expeditions in the still largely wooded landscape. Other evidence of Bronze Age farmers can be seen at Bracken Rigg where

the Pennine Way approaches Cronkley farm, where there are the earthwork remains of a hut circle sitting within its own fields.

The impression we get from these glimpses of the activities of early farmers of the late-Stone Age and bronze age are of gradually increasing, but still relatively small scale agricultural activity, probably accompanied by seasonal use of upland grazing and continued hunting of the wild boar, deer and wild cattle which inhabited the woods and grasslands.

This period of seemingly gradual change came to an end sometime in the late-Bronze Age and early-Iron Age when all over the Pennine uplands there was a massive and widespread loss of woodland cover. The precise cause of this period of woodland clearance is not obvious, but the evidence of pollen profiles in peat cores is very clear; levels of tree pollen fall very low as heather becomes a dominant plant in the uplands for the first time. This environmental evidence is backed up by the archaeology. The remains of Iron Age and Roman period settlements are now known to be widespread

Bracken Rigg Bronze Age Settlement: A large hut circle can be seen near the centre of the photograph, surrounded by the curving boundaries of a few small fields
© Martin Townsend (Valley Drone)

throughout the North Pennines. In Teesdale one of the best examples is at Forcegarth where two settlements occupied in the first century AD were excavated by Dennis and Ken and are surrounded by the remains of an extensive field system of small arable and pasture fields.

Roman rule in Britain effectively ended in the early fifth century AD. How quickly this affected Upper Teesdale is unclear but we do know that in the next five centuries there were several changes in language and religion. We can see the changes in language in place names; Holwick for instance is Anglo Saxon, the language of the first settlers after the retreat of the Roman Empire. By the middle of the seventh century life was probably quite settled in this remote part of the now Christian Kingdom of Northumbria. All this changed again with Viking coastal raids in the late eighth century culminating in Viking settlement and the establishment of the Viking territory of Danelaw in the ninth century. Upper Teesdale is right on the boundary between ninth century Northumbria and Danelaw and this is reflected by place names too: the many Teesdale settlements have Scandinavian names such as Micklethwaite, in contrast to the mainly Anglo Saxon place names in Weardale to the North. This contrast is even seen in the way features of the landscape are named today: in Weardale and further North a stream is called a burn and a waterfall is a linn, in Teesdale beck and force are used.

The impact of Scandinavian settlement is also visible on the ground, particularly on Holwick Fell where there are several small settlements with Norse style longhouses such as the farmsteads excavated by Dennis and Ken at Simy Folds. Here there were four farmsteads located within a complex of small rectangular fields and some much larger areas of enclosed fell. Although these settlements appear to have been occupied quite briefly, their existence suggests that Teesdale was a busy place in the late first millennium AD. Possibly this settlement and activity were connected with the long distance route now known as the Green Trod. Where this

Simy Folds Viking Settlement: the two farmyards in the picture include Norse style longhouses forming part of a small hamlet in an area of rectangular fields on a limestone bench
© Martin Townsend (Valley Drone)

crosses Cronkley Fell it is still referred to on the map as the Man Gate, an Anglo Saxon name meaning the common road.

It isn't clear how direct or immediate an effect the Norman Conquest and the subsequent Harrying of the North had on Teesdale or the rest or the North Pennines. We know that the Domesday Book records villages and towns as far up as the Tees and no further. Certainly the Anglo Scandinavian aristocracy was to a large extent replaced by Norman Lords. This is when many of what we think of as typical medieval villages, where farms were clustered together along streets or round a village green, were created out of an earlier more dispersed settlement pattern. This pattern of villages surrounded by open fields, and beyond that common grazing land, dominated from Middleton-in-Teesdale eastwards and can still be seen in the landscape. At Mickleton the long thin strips called tofts which formed the property boundaries of the medieval holdings can still be seen clearly, north and south of the village, and beyond that are the remains of terraces, or lynchets and ridge and furrow resulting from cultivation of strips in the medieval open fields.

West of Middleton the Norman Lords indulged their love of hunting and designated large areas as forests: areas for hunting venison (red deer and wild boar). In Teesdale the most significant forests were the Forest of Teesdale, north of the Tees, west of Middleton, and the Forest of Lune which extended south of the Tees from Holwick to the River Lune. The designation of much of Upper Teesdale as Forest affected the medieval landscape in several ways; in order to maintain the grasslands and woods in good productive condition for the deer they needed grazing, but not in such a way that competed with the deer. In general cattle and horses were preferred because they do not graze as closely as sheep and goats and do less damage to trees. The practice of shieling, seasonal grazing with cattle, which had probably been traditional since the Bronze Age, was supplemented by cattle ranches, called vaccaries, and stud farms for horses. In the middle of the twelfth century Bernard Baliol, Lord of Barnard Castle, granted extensive rights to the monks of Rievaulx Abbey for the pasturing of cattle and especially horses in Ettersgill, Hudeshope and Egglesburn. Such gifts by Norman Lords to monastic institutions were common in the medieval period in order to secure the future wellbeing of their souls.

Ore Pit Holes Medieval Mines: over a kilometre length of medieval ironstone mining shows as a line of grassy bumps and hollows where the mining has exposed lime-rich spoil © Martin Townsend (Valley Drone)

It is important to understand that medieval Forests were areas where particular laws applied for the preservation of the venison (red deer and wild boar) and vert (the woods and grazing), but not just areas of woodland; they could contain villages fields farms and moorland too, and often did. Forests were important as mineral royalties too, where the Lord typically took a tithe (or one tenth) of the metal produced. Both lead and iron smelting sites are known, exploiting deposits of ore associated with the mineral veins which abound in the North Pennines. Iron mining and smelting appears to have been much the most widespread of the two. Over fifty medieval iron smelting sites (known as bloomeries) are known on Holwick Fell alone. Most are small and may have been part of a domestic scale

Keld Smithy Medieval Iron
Furnace: a heap of slag next
to a spring marks the site of
a medieval iron furnace
© Tom Gledhill & Rose
Simpkins

industry conducted by villagers taking their cattle to shielings in the summer. Even at this small scale, huge quantities of charcoal were required to smelt and forge the iron. Amazingly the small pits in which the charcoal was made also still survive and can be found in intakes and around the fringes of the North Pennine fells. Nearly five hundred have been found on Holwick Fell in a survey by the author and Ros Nichol. This evidence of charcoal making and iron smelting suggests that the fringes of fells like Holwick Fell were covered in woodpasture, dominated by birch, but with many other tree species present such as alder, willow and hazel, and that such areas were a hive of industry, with people pasturing their cattle, mining, smelting and making charcoal.

Another period of change began in the fourteenth century with the start of a deterioration in the climate referred to as the little ice age. This was accompanied by cattle plague and the Great Famine of 1315-17 which affected most of Northern Europe, followed by the Black Death which reached Britain in in 1349 and is estimated to have to have killed 30-60% of Europe's population in a few years. This reduction in population had a profound impact on landscape and society. One effect was that there was more land to go round and in the long term Lords had to offer better terms to their tenants in order to retain them. As a result peasant farmers were more prosperous, more were able to eat meat, and there was less incentive to supplement their livings with domestic scale industries. This led to the progressive conversion of

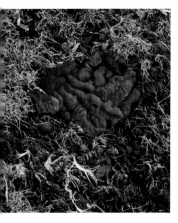

Medieval iron slag
© Tom Gledhill

former medieval arable to pasture and meadow, particularly in upland landscapes like Teesdale. Keeping stock was also less labour intensive so there was also a gradual reduction in the number of farms. This can be seen in Holwick. Volunteers working on the North Pennines AONB Partnership's Altogether Archaeology project, now an independent charity, have mapped the lynchets and ridge and furrow of the former open fields which survive in what are now species rich hay meadows. Between these they mapped the remains of the deserted medieval farmsteads which survive between the modern farms. Lack of labour resulted in the mechanisation of industry; water power replaced human muscle and the iron industry moved east to areas where there was woodland which could be sustainably managed as coppice and the investment in large scale smelting was worthwhile.

Lead mining and smelting are known to have been taking place in the North Pennines since at least the

Field Byre and Lynchets at Low Way: nearly two thousand years of Teesdale history in one photograph. The eighteenth-century byre in the centre is surrounded by a complex of parallel lynchets, evidence for medieval cultivation. The byre sits within an enclosure which was used in the eighteenth century as a stackyard for hay in the surrounding meadow, but probably originated as a Romano-British settlement. © Tom Gledhill & Rose Simpkins medieval period, but underwent a significant expansion in the eighteenth century. This was partly a response to higher demand, but was also facilitated by a change from small independent partnerships working small lengths of vein, to leases of longer lengths of vein, allowing greater investment, more efficient drainage and deeper mines. Ultimately by the early nineteenth century mining in Teesdale was dominated by the London Lead Company who built their headquarters in the small market town of Middleton. The expansion of lead mining not only led to the expansion of towns and villages, it also had a profound effect on the farming industry. Many miners were smallholders, occupying small dispersed tenant farms whose creation was facilitated by the enclosure of common meadows and pastures. The process of enclosure also created the landscape of dry stone walls, though in the early stages hedges may have played a much greater role than is generally acknowledged. In amongst the smallholdings were some large dairy farms, like Valance Lodge or Lune Head Farm, that supplied the burgeoning population of the Dale with milk, butter and cheese. Such farms can be identified by their relatively large size, and often by the presence of large stone cheese presses which can still sometimes be found. This period was probably the highpoint of Teesdale cow keeping and must have led to the creation of a significant area of new hay meadows, particularly in the upper Dale.

Wynch Bridge, Low Force
© Anne Kelly

The lead industry not only led to investment in the farming infrastructure, and the expansion of towns and villages, there were also improvements in transport, such as Wynch Bridge, first built in 1741 to allow miners from Holwick to reach their work places on the north side of the valley. Roads were built to take ore to

the smeltmills and lead to Newcastle. This culminated
in the construction of the railway to Barnard Castle in
1856 and Middleton-in-Teesdale in 1867, just in time to
facilitate the mass emigration of miners leaving for a
better life abroad in response to a downturn in the lead
industry caused by cheap imports from Europe,
particularly Spain.

Better transport and the invention of the breach
loaded shotgun in the nineteenth century led to the
development of grouse shooting. Seasonal burning has
probably been part of the management of upland
grazing since hunter gatherers first came to Teesdale
after the last glaciation, but the management of heather
for grouse is much more organised and widespread than
anything which has gone before, giving us the extensive
heather moorlands which are such a distinctive part of
the North Pennine landscape today. This is

Rotational heather burning
© Alistair Lockett

accompanied by predator control to encourage large numbers of red grouse for the shoot. As a by-product of this the North Pennines support both important populations of ground nesting birds such as curlew and lapwing and a robust rabbit population.

The Second World War led to the ploughing up of some pastures and meadows to grow potatoes and turnips, but this was just a blip in the post medieval pastoral farming of the Dale. Also, there were efforts to drain the extensive areas of blanket bog for growing crops which simply led to major deterioration of the peat. Sheep have become progressively more important to the farming economy of Teesdale since the agricultural improvements of the eighteenth century. They now form the backbone of the farming economy. What happens next only the future will tell, but two things are certain: man will continue to be a major factor in the ecology of the Dale, and that change in climate, ecology and landscape are inevitable, as they always have been.

Reference

Coggins, D, 'People in Upper Teesdale' in *The natural history of Upper Teesdale, 4th edition,* M E Bradshaw (ed.), 2003.

Chapter 2

Weather and climate

Ian Findlay

Introduction

Geographically, the Pennines are unique within England because they are the only significant upland area that is not close to the sea. This fact has implications for the climate of the Pennines and, with the River Tees having its source close to Cross Fell, the highest summit in the Pennine chain, Upper Teesdale has its own climatic conditions.

The Dale is also unique in having more data and long-term weather stations than any other UK upland area. A continuous temperature record is available from 1931 (Holden & Adamson, 2001). Gordon Manley of Durham University began recording at Moor House at 550 m in the 1950s, using a hut close to the summit of Great Dun Fell, the second highest Pennine summit (850 m). Designation of the area as a Site of Special

Scientific Interest in 1948, then National Nature Reserve in 1952, saw Moor House established as a Nature Conservation field station and daily recordings were made for almost 30 years.

Reservoirs built in Selset and Lunedale (1955) and Baldersdale (1960) took advantage of the heavy local rainfall, and despite strong opposition, Cow Green reservoir was built in the late 1960s. Significant funding was provided for research to monitor any changes associated with the reservoir, including the effect such a large body of water may have on micro-climate. A weather station was set up on Widdybank Fell (510 m) for daily recording, data being analysed by local universities and sent to the Met Office that took over the recording in 1974. Records were mostly made by Ian Findlay, until his retirement in 1996 when he relocated the weather station to his home at Hunt Hall Farm, Langdon Beck (370 m). He has continued recording ever since.

Hunt Hall Farm weather station
© Ian Findlay

What are conditions like?

Gordon Manley summarised the climate at high altitudes in the Pennines as follows; 'We therefore form a conception of excessively windy and pervasively wet autumn, a very variable and stormy winter with long spells of

snow cover, high humidity and extremely bitter wind, alternating with brief periods of rain and thaw. April has a mean temperature little above the freezing point and sunny days in May are offset by cold polar air, while the short and cloudy summer is not quite warm enough for the growth of trees. Throughout the year, indeed, the summers are frequently covered in cloud'.

This cool, wet climate has been central in dictating the range of vegetation and associated fauna in Upper Teesdale. Blanket bog, rare in a global context, is common above 500 m on limestone and other rock types. Climactic conditions allow some plant growth but only partial decomposition of dead material, the latter forming peat to a depth of around 2 m.

At the altitudes of 350 – 800 m in the Dale, the growing season is very short, even with 'the best weather', with implications for wildlife and hill farmers.

And the characteristic weather of uplands is the occurrence of extreme climatic events, such as the severe winters of 1916, 1940, 1947 (all with late winter and heavy snowfall), 1963 (prolonged snow cover and very cold) and 1978/79. Weather dictated the rate of farming practice, particularly up to 1960 when the horse was relied upon rather than the tractor. As late as 1979, the four-wheel drive tractor was a rare vehicle in the Dale!

For the past 25 years the Environment Agency has

Manley noted that the mean May temperatures at the summit station were similar to the mean January temperatures in London and he considered the climate in Upper Teesdale similar to that at sea level in Iceland!

asked all upland weather stations to record snowfall and to measure the depth and weight of snow, as well as rainfall during the winter. Such data are used in flood forecasting for the lowlands.

Records 1931 to 1999

Across this period the average temperature was 5.3°C, ranging from –18.5°C (31 January 1972) to 28.0°C (4 August 1990). On 23 August 1976, at Widdybank Fell, the maximum temperature was 23°C, followed by a minimum of –1.5°C, a range of 24.5°C. On average there was some rain on 244 days per year and 45 days per year were considered as foggy. The average days with air frost was 126 per year, with frost in every month.

Extreme weather events

1976: A very dry, hot summer reaching 18.6°C mean maximum in July and August. A wet autumn, with a total of 17.9" rain (September 8.6", October 9.3"), followed by low temperatures, high snowfall and heavy drifting in November, December.

1978: Snowfall in late December and two days of blizzards to end the year.

1979: A dreadful winter. Four separate periods of blizzards (severe, very severe, extreme) for two or three days and 129 consecutive days on cross-country skis. Local roads were blocked for long periods, Birkdale Farm was cut off by snow from 28 December to 16 April, local schools were closed and people couldn't get out of the Dale to their jobs. A very difficult time for the farming community.

1983: 8 July, following a thunderstorm a 1 – 1.5 m high roll on Maize Beck, two more later and then a final roll in late July — four rolls within three weeks! Rain fell at the rate of 6" per hour, washing peat off high ground, destroying two bridges and washing away walls.

Arctic conditions
© Anne Kelly

1985: Very wet (23") in July and August, delaying hay making until September / October (first use of big bales).

1986: Much freezing rain, (11.8") in January with several days of ice, 9 days of blizzards and severe drifting in February, mean maximum temperature –2.5°C, mean minimum air temperature –6.4°C. Up to 35 cm snow in February/March. Five different thermometer readings (maximum, air minimum, grass minimum, wet and dry bulb) were below zero for 31 days — a record. Total rainfall 80.2". One of the coldest months of the century.

High Force in spate, 1995
© Ian Findlay

1992: Severe gales on 2/3 January, average wind speed 60 mph over 24 hours (gusts 80 – 90 mph) caused severe tree damage at High Force and felled 700+ trees. Yet unbelievably, seven days later in the month were completely calm!

1995: 4" rain fell over 48 hours on 30 January (50.2 mm) and 31 January (47.9 mm). A rapid 7°C rise in temperature triggered a sudden thaw of large amounts of snow on the fells, producing the biggest becks and River Tees since 1968. The Environment Agency issued flood warnings for the lowland areas.

Low rainfall totals for June, July, August (only 0.6", the lowest on record), high sunshine totals and high temperatures (August mean maximum temperature 19.9°C). Many areas with shallow soils were burnt out, Cow Green reservoir was so low that the ruins of the mine shop and construction road were exposed in late summer.

1996: The January sunshine total of 6.9 hours was a record low (the average is 35.0 hours).

Records in the new millennium

Weather patterns from 2000 have seen a slight change as the summary on the following pages shows.

The figures on the following tables must be read with the understanding that they reflect the weather patterns only in Upper Teesdale, which covers large areas of the uplands varying in height from 350 m to 700 m. At these altitudes the growing season is very short.

The facts and figures highlight that in any given year farming / wildlife has to cope with complex weather conditions.

Year	Annual rainfall total	Rain days	Sunshine hours	Mean of maximum temperature °C / number of days over 20°C		Mean of minimum temperature °C		Snow days		Diary note
2000	1,841.5 mm, 72.5" November 307.3 mm, 12.1"	273 Very high	1,328.7 May 208.4 below average	May June July August	13.3 (2) 15.0 (3) 15.9 (1) 17.1 (1)	May June July August	4.1 7.4 8.1 8.6	January 2 February 9 March 5 Total 16		A very wet year
2001	1,181.1 mm, 42.5"	241	1,400.6 May 248 Average sunshine total	May June July August	14.5 (3) 14.1 (2) 17.1 (9) 17.0 (4)	May June July August	4.0 7.1 9.9 8.2	January 9 February 9 March 15 April 1 Total 34		Average rainfall Very dry summer
2002	1,620.5 mm, 63.8" February 373.4 mm, 14.7"	230	1,211.5 Very low	May June July August	12.2 (0) 14.7 (0) 16.2 (2) 18.8 (7)	May June July August	5.8 8.0 8.3 10.5	January 5 February 6 March 15 December 1 Total 27		February 14.7" rain a record Very low sunshine total
2003	998.2 mm, 39.3"	197 Low	1,644.2 June 208.0 August 203.1 Above average sunshine	May June July August	12.9 (2) 17.3 (3) 18.4 (8) 19.1 (13)	May June July August	5.5 8.3 10.4 9.5	January 12 February 6 March 11 Total 29		Low rainfall, high sunshine total, high temperatures
2004	1,435.1 mm, 56.5" August 274.3 mm, 10.8"	258 High	1,383.0 May 234 Below average sunshine	May June July August	14.3 (0) 16.0 (2) 16.8 (6) 18.0 (7)	May June July August	4.2 7.6 8.8 10.6	January 10 February 8 March 5 November 1 December 6 Total 30		Below average sunshine Very wet August 10.8"
2005	1,244.6 mm, 49.0"	240	1,427.3 May 222.6 Average sunshine total	May June July August	12.2 (0) 16.5 (5) 17.7 (7) 17.1 (3)	May June July August	4.3 8.0 9.5 8.5	January 5 February 9 March 10 November 4 December 4 Total 32		Average rainfall, sunshine total Low summer months

Year	Annual rainfall total	Rain days	Sunshine hours	Mean of maximum temperature °C / number of days over 20°C		Mean of minimum temperature °C		Snow days		Diary note
2006	1,475.7 mm, 58.1" December 335.0 mm, 13.2"	224	1,639.4 May 201.0 June 203.1 July 299.6	May June July August	13.4 (2) 17.4 (10) 22.0 (22) 16.2 (3)	May June July August	4.5 7.7 9.4 9.2	January February March April Total 22	1 6 14 1	July very warm, 22.0°C highest Sunshine 299.6 hours Also highest record for one month (July)
2007	1,430.0 mm, 56.3"	214	1,513.5 April 214.1	May June July August	12.6 (0) 16.2 (4) 16.2 (0) 16.2 (2)	May June July August	4.4 8.0 8.9 8.8	January February March December Total 15	6 4 4 1	Very wet June and July
2008	1,663.7 mm, 65.5"	247	1,327.9 May 209.7	May June July August	14.6 (2) 14.9 (1) 17.5 (6) 16.2 (0)	May June July August	4.9 6.7 9.7 10.6	January February March April October November December Total 36	7 1 7 3 1 3 14	Very wet June, July and September
2009	1,524.0 mm, 60.0" November 432.5 mm, 17.0"	247	1,501.3 May 232.6	May June July August	13.0 (2) 16.4 (7) 16.9 (3) 17.0 (1)	May June July August	4.7 6.8 9.4 9.0	January February March November December Total 44	13 14 1 1 15	Very wet November, 17.0", highest record for one month
2010	1,074.4 mm, 42.3"	224	1,519.5 May 202.2 July 222.8 Average sunshine	May June July August	12.3 (4) 17.0 (7) 16.5 (2) 16.1 (1)	May June July August	2.8 7.1 9.9 8.2	January February March November December Total 76	27 17 1 6 25	High snowfall January, February. December high snowfall, Max 0.9°C Min −5.4°C River Tees frozen 6-8" ice
2011	1,412.2 mm, 55.6"	246	1,495.1 April 219.6 May 214.3	May June July August	12.8 (0) 15.1 (4) 16.9 (5) 15.5 (1)	May June July August	4.9 6.5 7.1 8.2	January February March December Total 29	8 6 2 13	Quick thaw eary January Below average sunshine in summer months

Year	Annual rainfall total	Rain days	Sunshine hours	Mean of maximum temperature °C / number of days over 20°C		Mean of minimum temperature °C		Snow days		Diary note
2012	1,595.1mm, 62.8"	233	1,383.6 May 218.6 June 94.7 lowest record for June	May 13.1 (6) June 13.4 (0) July 15.4 (0) August 17.2 (4)		May 3.5 June 7.1 July 9.3 August 9.2		January 4 February 7 April 3 December 10 Total 24		Low sunshine total Wet summer, autumn and winter
2013	1,384.3mm, 54.5"	214 Low	1,433.4 July 269.0 second highest sunshine total	May 12.0 (1) June 15.6 (0) July 20.6 (19) August 17.4 (5)		May 3.9 June 6.3 July 10.3 August 9.8		January 15 February 14 March 22 April 5 December 1 Total 57		Average rainfall early year Wet backend Very cold March (Max 2.2°C Min −2.8°C) Very warm July
2014	1,422.4mm, 56.0"	231	1,375.9 July 247.1	May 13.0 (1) June 16.7 (1) July 19.4 (12) August 15.5 (1)		May 6.0 June 7.9 July 19.4 August 15.5		January 3 February 6 March 1 December 6 Total 16		Very wet January and February Very dry June (1.3") July (1.5") and September (0.6") Rainfall total 1.5" more than last year
2015	1,724.7mm, 67.9" December 492.0mm, 19.4"	237	1,480.5 April 237.5	May 10.9 (0) June 14.7 (3) July 16.1 (4) August 16.6 (1)		May 3.8 June 6.0 July 7.7 August 8.9		January 12 February 13 March 1 November 3 December 3 Total 32		Second highest rainfall total after 2000 December rainfall total 19.4" highest monthly total since 1968 Higher winter temps! Lower summer temps! Higher number of snow days!
2016	1,137mm, 44.8"	201 Low	1,399.6 2 July 27.2°C	May 13.8 (2) June 16.0 (3) July 16.8 (4) August 16.9 (4)		May 4.1 June 7.5 July 9.4 August 9.3		January 8 February 4 March 3 April 3 November 5 Total 23		Low rainfall for the year Snow recorded in 5 months but for short periods Average sunshine totals
2017	1,155.7mm, 45.5"	235	1,427.8 May 221.5	May 14.8 (4) June 15.9 (5) July 16.5 (2) August 16.0 (1)		May 5.2 June 8.5 July 8.5 August 8.8		January 6 February 5 March 3 November 1 December 14 Total 29		Below average rainfall. Very dry April and May. Wet period June - October Cold December - 14 snow days, 18 days ground frost, 17 days air frost

The implications of change

Since 2000 the weather pattern has altered, with extremes of rainfall, sunshine and strong winds. Winters have had less snowfall and periods of snow cover measured in weeks, not months. Climate change is not new, but does impact on wildlife and affects the farming year with implications for the farming community, flora and fauna.

Wet open winters with a higher rainfall delay ground warming in the spring affecting invertebrate eggs and overwintering pupae, including those of moths, that are the food for early nesting wader chicks. Slow growth of vegetation delays suckler cows and their calves being turned out into pastures by two or three weeks, at extra feed cost to the farmer.

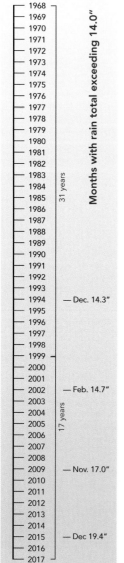

The timeline shows the occurrence of months with rainfall exceeding 14.0".
It seems to be getting wetter.
This view is supported by very recent records of total rainfall and rain days over three consecutive months

November 2015   11.5", 27 rain days
December 2015   19.4", 30 rain days
January 2016   9.2", 27 rain days

Total 40.2", 84 rain days

A surge of bracken growth on the lower fells, especially in juniper woodlands, cannot be managed by chemical treatment and is associated with less snow cover and fewer frost days. Rush species have spread extensively in pastures and wet ground areas in the Dale due to lower cattle grazing, but open winters and high rainfall do not help.

1979 — the dreadful winter. B6277 near Langdon Beck Hotel.
© Ian Findlay

The rabbit population is higher on the high fells; previously hard winters kept rabbits under control. Fewer sheep graze the upland sites allowing blue moor-grass *(Sesleria caerulea)* to dominate areas to the detriment of rare plants. A similar increase in bog asphodel *(Narthecium ossifragum)* puts sheep, particularly lambs, at risk because of the plant's high toxicity.

Rushes
© Steve Gater

Heavy and sudden rainfall has caused damage to road foundations and drains, cutting off the B6277, the only access road running east to west in the Dale. Since the road is built on glacial till and runs close to the Tees, it is at risk from future weather extremes.

The challenge for the future is to reduce atmospheric emissions to minimise the human-induced component of climate change and devise appropriate land management strategy. That would encourage the survival of the highly valued Upper Teesdale flora and fauna.

References and further reading

Holden, J & Adamson, J K (2001), *Gordon Manley and the North Pennines*, Journal of Meteorology 26, 329-333.

Holden, J & Adamson, J K (2002), *The Moor House long-term upland temperature record: new evidence of recent warming*, Weather, **57**, 119-127.

Manley, G (1942), *Meteorological observations on Dun Fell, a mountain station in northern England*, Quarterly Journal of the Royal Meteorological Society, **68**, 151-165.

Manley, G (1980), *The northern Pennines revisited: Moor House, 1932-78*, Meteorological Magazine, **109**, 281-292.

Simply stunning
© Anne Kelly

Chapter 3

Bedrock geology

Brian Young

Introduction

The underlying rocks, and the earth processes that have created them over millions of years, are an essential part of any area's natural history. The variety of rocks shapes the landscape, provides the foundation for soils – and thus plant and animal life – and profoundly influences the lives of human inhabitants.

Nowhere is this connection clearer than in Upper Teesdale. Whereas there is much of interest in the rocks, fossils and minerals themselves, an understanding of this geological diversity is also vital to fully appreciating the ecological, social and economic character of this beautiful Pennine valley.

The significance of its geology figures prominently in Upper Teesdale's place within the Moor House–Upper

Teesdale National Nature Reserve and the North Pennines Area of Outstanding Natural Beauty (AONB) which coincides with the North Pennines UNESCO Global Geopark. Numerous sites and features within the Dale are scheduled as Sites of Special Scientific Interest (SSSIs) specifically for their geological importance.

Upper Teesdale has attracted research interest since the earliest days of geological science, resulting in a voluminous technical literature. Drawing upon this, and following a brief outline of the Dale's geological history, this chapter introduces some of the most important aspects of the rocks and landscape we see around us today, including places where geological features of interest may be seen, and highlights the relevance of these to other aspects of the Dale's natural and human history. For readers wishing to explore Upper Teesdale's geology in greater depth, a list of useful texts is offered.

Low Force. The dolerite of the Whin Sill here forms rapids in the River Tees.
© Steve Gater

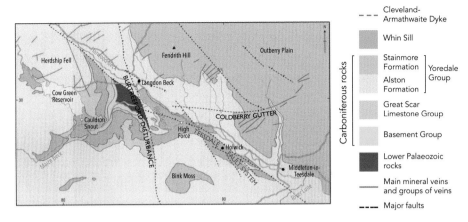

Figure 1: Simplified geological map depicting the bedrock geology of the Dale.
NB. For clarity, many mineral veins and some faults are omitted.

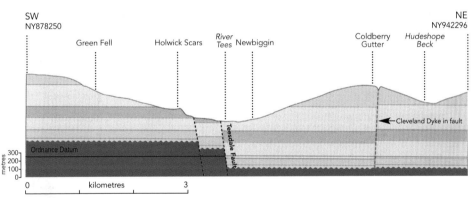

Figure 2: Simplified section through Teesdale Fault (structure below Whin Sill is conjectural)

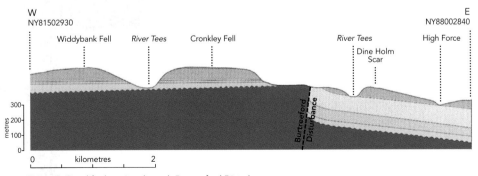

Figure 3: Simplified section through Burtreeford Disturbance

A brief geological history

The rocks visible today in Upper Teesdale record almost 500 million years of earth history.

The periods of earth history represented, together with the materials formed at those times are:

Superficial (drift) deposits: more detail is given in Chapter 4
(Unconsolidated deposits, mainly formed by glacial action and later processes within the past 2.6 million years, and which mantle and conceal the underlying bedrock - commonly referred to by geologists as 'Drift' deposits).

Bedrock:
(The hard, bedrock formed over millions of years of geological history – commonly referred to by geologists as 'Solid' deposits)

Palaeogene (Tertiary)
>> Basalt of the Armathwaite-Cleveland Dyke

Upper Palaeozoic
> *Late Carboniferous-Early Permian*
>> Mineral veins
>> Dolerite of the Whin Sill
> *Carboniferous*
>> Beds composed mainly of limestone, shale, sandstone and some thin coal seams, many times repeated with beds of pebbly conglomerate at the base.
> *Devonian*
>> Emplacement of Weardale Granite into Ordovician rocks of the North Pennines

Lower Palaeozoic
> *Ordovician rocks*
>> Volcanic rocks and slates

The oldest rocks known in Northern England date from the Ordovician and Silurian periods of earth history, between 480 and 420 million years ago. At this time the portions of the earth's crust that would eventually become Britain lay south of the equator on either side of a deep ocean, known by geologists as the Iapetus Ocean. To the north of the ocean lay the ancient continent of Laurentia, which included the area that would become Scotland; on its southern side lay Avalonia, which included the area destined to include England and Wales. Movement of the earth's tectonic plates caused these two continents to move inexorably closer, eventually colliding around 420 million years ago, resulting in the major mountain-building episode known as the Caledonian Orogeny. Muds and sands, deposited on the floor of Iapetus were squeezed and deformed to form hard sandstones and slates, and volcanic eruptions caused by the collision created vast volumes of lava and ash. In addition, huge masses of molten rock, or magma, which never reached the surface, solidified to form enormous bodies of granite, including the Weardale Granite that underlies much of the North Pennines. A huge mountain chain was thus created over what is now Scotland and Northern England. These are the rocks we see today forming the mountains of the Lake District. Exactly similar rocks of this age lie hidden at depth beneath most of Northern England but, as a result of later earth movements, small slices of these have been pushed to the surface along the Pennine escarpment and in Upper Teesdale.

Following this dramatic episode, continuing movement of the tectonic plates gradually brought the area close to the equator by about 350 million years ago, at the beginning of the Carboniferous period. By then, millions of years of erosion had worn down these mountains to their roots, in what is now Northern England, though substantial mountains remained in the area now occupied by the Scottish Highlands, the northern North Sea and Scandinavia. Much of what was to become Northern Britain was gradually submerged beneath a shallow tropical sea. Rendered more buoyant by the huge underlying mass of the Weardale Granite, the earth's crust beneath the area destined to form the North Pennines initially remained as an area of relatively higher land, though with time even this became submerged beneath the extensive Carboniferous sea. Within the clear warm waters of this sea an abundance of marine life created thick accumulations of limestone.

Instability caused by continuing earth movements caused huge rivers draining the mountains to the north and north east to carry enormous amounts of mud and sand into the sea, repeatedly building extensive coastal swamps and deltas upon which lush tropical rainforests developed. Over the ensuing 50 million years, continuing instability and repeated episodes of global climate change resulted in flooding by the sea alternating with the growth of deltas and coastal swamps. The result was a series of cyclical successions, known as 'cyclothems', with the cycle of limestone, shale, sandstone and coal repeated many times. Limestones and shales were formed as marine sediments and the coals and many of the sandstones formed under freshwater swamp and deltaic conditions. With time, the marine intervals became fewer and briefer, resulting in more numerous sandstones and coal seams, culminating towards the end of Carboniferous times with extensive swamp forests that formed the coal seams of the Coal Measures.

At the beginning of Permian times, stretching of the Earth's crust caused huge volumes of molten rock (magma) to rise up from the earth's mantle. This did not reach the surface, but spread out horizontally between the layers of Carboniferous rocks where it cooled and crystallised to form the bed of rock known as the Whin Sill. Heat from this magma severely altered, or metamorphosed, the rocks into which it came into contact, baking limestones to form marble, known locally as 'sugar limestone'. Specialised analytical techniques enable us to date the cooling and crystallisation of the Whin Sill at around 295 million years ago.

Holwick Scars. The Whin Sill here forms high crags in which columnar joining is conspicuous
© Brian Young

At about this time, earth movements bent the Carboniferous rocks into a gentle dome-like structure sometimes referred to as the Teesdale Dome. In consequence, over much of Upper Teesdale the Carboniferous rocks dip gently to the east. This folding was accompanied by some fracturing of the rocks to create faults – fractures along which the rocks have been displaced relative to one another. Two of these, illustrated in Figures 2 and 3, are very significant in shaping the Teesdale landscape.

The Teesdale Fault is a major northwest-southeast trending fracture along which the rocks on its northern side have been displaced downwards by up to several tens of metres relative to those on its southern side (Figure 2). In consequence, the Whin Sill, so conspicuously seen on the south side of the Dale, lies far beneath the surface on its northern side. Like many such large faults, the Teesdale Fault is a belt of roughly parallel fractures. The course of the River Tees has been largely determined by the relative ease by which the fractured rocks adjacent to the fault have been eroded.

The second major structure to affect Teesdale's landscape is the rather complex north-south trending belt of folding and faulting known as the Burtreeford Disturbance, a major structural feature that bisects the North Pennines. As may be seen in Figure 3, this displaces the Carboniferous rocks downwards by several tens of metres on its eastern side. Geological mapping reveals that this displacement occurred both before and after the intrusion of the Whin Sill. Because there are very few exposures of the Burtreeford Disturbance it remains a poorly understood feature of the local geology.

Upper Teesdale's rocks are cut by numerous smaller faults which, soon after the intrusion of the Whin Sill, were filled with minerals to create the mineral veins which were the basis for the Dale's long history of metalliferous mining.

From the formation of the Whin Sill and the area's

mineral veins at around 295 million years ago, the record of geological events that affected Teesdale's geology falls silent until about 60 million years ago in the Palaeogene period. By then plate tectonics had moved the area close to its present latitude. Stretching of the earth's tectonic plates created a new split in the crust which heralded the opening of the Atlantic Ocean. This fracturing was accompanied by violent volcanic activity in what is now the Hebrides and Northern Ireland. Fractures radiating from the volcanic centre on the Isle of Mull extended as far as Northern England and acted as conduits for basaltic magma. One of these basalt-filled fractures, known as the Cleveland-Armathwaite Dyke, crosses the North Pennines and crops out at several places in Teesdale. The emplacement of this dyke marks the final recorded event in the history of Upper Teesdale's bedrock, or 'solid', geology. Chapter 4 covers the last 2.6 million years of landscape develeopment

Ordovician rocks

Whereas throughout the North Pennines Lower Palaeozoic rocks almost everywhere lie deeply buried beneath the younger Carboniferous rocks, they crop out at the surface on the Pennine escarpment and in Upper Teesdale. Elsewhere they have been proved in a handful of deep boreholes.

In Upper Teesdale, rocks of Ordovician age crop out beneath Cronkley Scar near Langdon Beck in an area known to geologists as the Teesdale Inlier. Although this extends over several square kilometres, it is mostly concealed beneath later Quaternary deposits with exposures limited to the banks and bed of the Tees between Cronkley Scar and Widdybank Farm.

Pale greenish-grey slates are exposed in an old quarry on the south side of the river at Pencil Mill [NY84802960] where they were once worked for the making of slate pencils, known locally as 'Widdies'. Rare fossils of the graptolites *Didymograptus* and *Glyptograptus*, together with samples of the microfossils known as acritarchs, collected here, indicate that these are of Lower Ordovician age and thus equivalent to parts of the Skiddaw Slates of the Lake District. The slates are cut by several vertical bodies, or dykes, of an igneous rock known as lamprophyre, which here form conspicuous low craggy exposures in the bed and banks of the river.

Fragments of partially formed slate pencils collected from the spoil heaps adjacent to the old Pencil Mill
© Brian Young

In the bed of the Tees a short distance upstream [NY83857966] is a very small exposure of silicified volcanic ash, or tuff, which is regarded as the equivalent of the volcanic rocks of the Borrowdale Volcanic Group of the Lake District.

Devonian rocks

Lying within the Lower Palaeozoic rocks of the North Pennines is the Weardale Granite, proved in a deep borehole drilled in Rookhope, Weardale, in 1961. Radiometric dating of this rock reveals that it was intruded, or emplaced, about 399 million years ago during the Devonian period of earth history. Although the granite nowhere reaches the surface, as noted above, it influenced the deposition of the overlying Carboniferous rocks and played an essential role in the formation of the area's mineral veins.

Although very small areas of Devonian sedimentary rocks occur locally in a few parts of the Pennine escarpment, no such rocks of this age are known from Upper Teesdale.

Carboniferous rocks

Since previous editions of this book, research into the Carboniferous geology of the UK has resulted in major revisions of the understanding and naming of these rocks. The following is a simplified summary of the current classification of these rocks within Upper Teesdale:

Pennine Coal Measures Group

| Yoredale Group | Stainmore Formation |
| | Alston Formation |

Great Scar Limestone Group

Basement Group

unconformity

Lower Palaeiozoic Rocks, including Northern Pennine Batholith

Within these Carboniferous rocks, all of the limestones, many of the sandstones, and some of the shales have names which reflect some characteristic feature of that unit. The names are a legacy of the area's mining and quarrying past and were coined by generations of miners and quarrymen who developed a sophisticated knowledge of the local Carboniferous stratigraphy. Many of the names survive as the formal names in use today in geological science.

Although the term 'Millstone Grit' was previously applied to sandstone-rich parts of the Northern Pennine Carboniferous succession, these sandstones are distinctive both in their character and depositional environment from the classic 'Millstone Grit' of the South Pennines and Derbyshire and the term is inappropriate in this area. These Northern Pennine sandstones are today included within the uppermost parts of the Stainmore formation.

Basement Group

Whereas the unconformable junction of the Carboniferous beds with the underlying Ordovician rocks is not exposed in Teesdale, the Carboniferous Basement Group which includes conglomerates composed predominantly of pebbles Skiddaw Slate and vein quartz, together with thin beds of shales and sandstones, crop out on Cronkley Scar and in the banks of the Tees adjacent to the Pennine Way at Falcon Clints [NY83402900].

Great Scar Limestone Group

Overlying the Basement Group is a thick limestone known, from its type location on the Pennine escarpment, as the Melmerby Scar Limestone. In Teesdale this is up to 38 m thick and is typically a pale grey, thinly- to thickly-bedded marine limestone, commonly with thin clay partings and locally with a rather rubbly appearance, especially near its top. The Melmerby Scar Limestone, together with the much thinner overlying Robinson and Peghorn limestones and the intervening thin beds of shale and sandstone, which are today correlated with the Great Scar Limestone Group of the Yorkshire Pennines, correspond with the Lower Limestone Group of earlier classifications. Good exposures of them may be seen on Cow Green [NY815310], Widdybank [NY825300] and

Cronkley fells [NY843290] where they are much altered adjacent to the Whin Sill (see below).

Yoredale Group

This group of Carboniferous rocks, which occupies the greater part of Upper Teesdale, comprises a succession of distinctive rock sequences repeated many times. As outlined above these record the repeated effects of crustal instability and global climate change over a period of roughly 50 million years. The resulting individual repeated sequences of sedimentary rock, or 'cyclothems', are known in the Pennines as 'Yoredale cyclothems' from Yoredale, the old name for Wensleydale in Yorkshire, where they were originally recognised and studied in great detail.

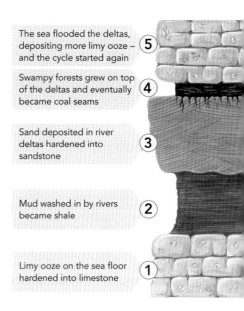

The sea flooded the deltas, depositing more limy ooze – and the cycle started again (5)

Swampy forests grew on top of the deltas and eventually became coal seams (4)

Sand deposited in river deltas hardened into sandstone (3)

Mud washed in by rivers became shale (2)

Limy ooze on the sea floor hardened into limestone (1)

A highly simplified section through a typical Yoredale cyclothem with interpretations of the conditions under which each rock type formed
© Elizabeth Pickett

Although marine fossils, including brachiopods, corals and crinoids, are comparatively abundant in most limestones, they are not always easily seen, and are usually more conspicuous on weathered surfaces. Some of the sandstones contain fossilised animal trails or burrows and fossilised plant roots and stems are also common, especially in so-called 'seatearths' (fossil soils) which may be overlain by a thin coal seam.

The Yoredale Group corresponds roughly with the Middle and Upper Limestone groups of earlier classifications, and includes those beds previously termed 'Millstone Grit'.

The Yoredale Group is divided into a lower division referred to as the Alston Formation, in which numerous limestones are major components of the succession.

Dark grey cyclindrical shafts of Frosterley Marble in the thirteenth-century Early English Gothic pillars of the Chapel of the Nine Altars, Durham Cathedral. Reproduced by kind permission of the Chapter of Durham Cathedral

Above the Great Limestone is the division known as the Stainmore Formation in which limestones are fewer and much thinner, with sandstones typically much more numerous and thicker; thin coal seams, some of which have been worked locally, are more common in the Stainmore Formation.

Examples of Yoredale Group limestones include the Tynebottom Limestone which forms the bed of the River South Tyne near Alston, the Scar Limestone which forms distinctive scar-like features locally, the Five Yard Limestone which is usually around 4.5 m thick, and the Great Limestone, the thickest limestone within the Yoredale Group. This latter limestone, typically up to 18 m thick, is of interest for several distinctive beds within it which can be recognised widely across the area. Particularly distinctive is the so-called 'Frosterley Band', a bed, up to about 1 m thick approximately 6 m below the top of the limestone, rich in fossils of the solitary coral *Dibunophyllum bipartitum*.

A polished slab of Frosterley Marble showing sections through the coral *Dibunophyllum bipartitum*. The scale bar is in cms.
© Brian Young

It has been worked as an ornamental stone, under the name of 'Frosterley Marble', fine examples of which can be seen in many churches, most notably Durham Cathedral. The Four Fathom Limestone, typically close to 7.3 m (4 fathoms = 24 feet) in thickness, recalls the local lead miners' practice of measuring in fathoms.

Most of the Dale's limestones have been worked to make quicklime for use as mortar or as a soil improver and small ruinous limekilns may be seen adjacent to many old quarries.

Within Upper Teesdale the Tynebottom Limestone forms the base of High Force [NY88002838] where at water level it has been eroded into a series of solution cavities. The Cockleshell Limestone is spectacularly exposed on the north bank of the Tees at Scoberry Bridge [NY91042734] where large shells of the brachiopod *Gigantoproductus* and crinoid stems are conspicuous on the water-worn surfaces. The Scar Limestone is seen in the old quarry adjacent to Langdon Beck Youth Hostel [NY86023048] and in Bowlees Quarry [NY90762842] alongside the footpath to Gibson's Cave. The Five Yard Limestone forms the lip of Summerhill Force at Gibson's Cave, Bowlees. The Great Limestone forms the

Gibson's Cave, also known as Summerhill Force. The Bowlees Beck here tumbles over the overhanging ledge formed by the Five Yard Limestone. The underlying shales and sandstone are visible in the 'cave' behind the fall.
© Brian Young

conspicuous scarp of High Hurth Edge [NY86503130] where the entrance to the Teesdale or Moking Hurth Cave, also in this limestone, may be seen. The old quarries in Hudeshope [NY94852725], north of Middleton, worked the Great Limestone. Typical fragments of the coral-rich Frosterley Band can sometimes be seen in old lead mine dumps further up this valley.

Many of the sandstones, known colloquially by the miners as 'hazle', were also given distinctive names, for example the Six Fathom Hazle (from its thickness), the Nattrass Gill Hazle (from its type location near Alston) and the Slaty Hazle (from the ease with which it could be split into thin slabs suitable for roofing).

To those unfamiliar with Northern Pennine rock nomenclature many of the sandstone names may seem curious as they are commonly referred to as 'sills', for example the Grindstone Sill (from its use in making grindstones), the Firestone Sill (from its use in making hearths and furnace linings) and the Slate Sill (from its breaking into thin slabs). 'Sill' was originally a Northern Pennine miners' term for any roughly horizontal body of rock. As will be explained below, its use to describe what we now know as the Whin Sill led to its adoption as the term for such intrusive bodies worldwide.

Sandstone has long been the stone of choice for building both in Teesdale and across the North Pennines. Many of the sandstones provided blocks suitable for farm buildings as well as the many miles of drystone walls. A few easily-split sandstones were worked to give the distinctive sandstone roofing slabs still seen on many of the Dale's older buildings. A hard siliceous sandstone known as ganister, used both for building and for refractory furnace linings, was worked in extensive quarries on either side of the road at Harthope Pass [NY86054476] between Teesdale and Weardale.

Good exposures of the Low Brig Hazle, the sandstone between the Scar and Five Yard Limestone, may be seen in the Bowlees Beck [NY90902858] between Bowlees and Gibson's Cave. The Firestone Sill forms prominent scarp features along the northern side of the Dale north of Langdon Beck [NY86503200] and above High Hurth Edge. The Low Grit Sills sandstone is exposed in the north walls of Coldberry Gutter [NY93102895] and both the Low and High Grit Sills sandstones form conspicuous bench features on the sides of the Hudeshope Valley.

Much of the scenic character of the Dale's landscape results directly from the character of these rocks.

Resistant rocks such as limestones and sandstones typically form steep, and in places craggy, bench-like features on hillsides or flat summits to many of the fells, for example Cross Fell [NY687343]; weaker rocks such as shales characteristically weather to gentle slopes, or slacks, between the benches.

Coal Measures

The Stainmore formation is overlain by a succession of similar sandstones and shales distinguished by the relative abundance of persistent coal seams, and known today as the Pennine Coal Measures Group, formerly extensively worked in the adjacent Durham Coalfield. Whereas Coal Measures rocks are present in the easternmost parts of Teesdale, because their outcrops are small and have little influence on the landscape, they are not considered further here.

The Whin Sill

Some of the most characteristic features of Teesdale's landscape, which distinguish this from all other Pennine dales, are extensive outcrops of the Whin Sill. Composed of the hard dark-grey igneous rock dolerite, this comprises a roughly horizontal sheet-like body that underlies much of North East England, including the North Pennines, and central and eastern Northumberland. As already noted in the discussion of geological history, the Whin Sill was intruded into the area's Carboniferous rocks as molten magma towards the end of Carboniferous times, about 295 million years ago. In Upper Teesdale it is up to 75 m thick. Because the molten magma from which it crystallised was injected at temperatures of around 1100°C, the adjacent rocks were severely altered, or metamorphosed. Limestones such as the Melmerby Scar Limestone were altered to coarse-grained white marble, known from its characteristic crumbly weathering as 'Sugar Limestone'; shales were baked to form a very hard rock known as hornfels. The local lead miners referred to this as 'whetstone', though it is not known whether it was ever used for making sharpening stones, or whetstones. Recent research has revealed the presence of widespread occurrences of magnetite in the altered Carboniferous rocks adjacent to the sill on Cronkley Fell, Cowgreen and beneath Falcon Clints.

The Whin Sill is of interest as being the original 'sill' of geological science. It takes its name from the north of England quarryman's term 'sill' for any more or less horizontal body of rock, combined with the term 'whin', meaning a hard black rock that was difficult to work, and which is said to derive from the 'whinn…' noise made when fragments are broken from it. The recognition of its intrusive origin, in the nineteenth century, led to the term 'sill' being adopted by geological science worldwide for all such horizontal intrusions of this sort.

The resistant Whin Sill dolerite gives Teesdale its famous waterfalls at High Force [NY88002838], Low Force [NY90302800] and Cauldron Snout [NY81402868]. The sombre line of dark grey crags, in which vertical columnar joints are conspicuous, at Holwick [NY903269] and Cronkley Scars [NY841294] on the southern side of the Dale, reflect the effects of the Teesdale Fault which displaces the sill down by several tens of metres below present levels of exposure on its northern side (Figure 2). Unusual rendzina soils, developed on the 'Sugar Limestone' at Cow Green [NY815310] and

Sugar Limestone. At the White Well on the top of Cronkley Fell, a spring rises from the junction of the crumbly weathering white marble with the underlying dolerite of the Whin Sill.
© Brian Young

High Force
© Matt Gater

Widdybank Fell [NY825300], support parts of the 'Teesdale assemblage' of rare arctic-alpine plant species, including Teesdale's beautiful iconic flower, the vivid blue spring gentian (*Gentiana verna*). Fine examples of the baked shale or 'whetstone' may be seen alongside the footpath to High Force and adjacent to the Pennine Way downstream from Wynch Bridge [NY90702760].

Whin Sill dolerite has long been an important source of roadstone and aggregate and large abandoned quarries scar its outcrop on the southern side of the Dale between Middleton-in-Teesdale [NY949246] and Holwick [NY897272]. Extraction continues from a large, but well-screened, quarry [NY87252830] a short distance upstream from High Force.

The Cleveland-Armathwaite dyke

Completing the Dale's suite of 'solid' rocks is the Cleveland-Armathwaite Dyke, an intrusion of dark-grey basalt of Palaeogene age which forms part of the swarm of intrusions centred upon the Hebridean island of Mull.

This dyke crops out intermittently across northern England between the Solway and Yorkshire coasts, including at several places on Alston Moor. In Teesdale, it crops out near Ettersgill [NY8846 2954], in Coldberry Gutter [NY92922894] and in Eggleston Burn [NY98972512]. Recent research has identified a hitherto unknown portion of the dyke within the Teesdale Fault in the Harwood Valley [NY805342], concealed at shallow depth beneath Carboniferous rocks and Quaternary deposits.

Mineral veins

The Carboniferous rocks and Whin Sill are cut by numerous small faults which, soon after the intrusion of the Whin Sill, acted as channels for the passage of mineral-rich solutions warmed by heat from the concealed Weardale Granite. As these cooled their contained minerals crystallised within the fault channels to form the mineral veins which provided the basis for the Dale's long history of mining.

The veins, which vary in width from a few millimetres up to over 10 m in rare instances, typically consist predominantly of assemblages of gangue, or 'spar' minerals including fluorite, baryte and quartz, accompanied by smaller amounts of ore minerals such as galena and sphalerite. Adjoining many veins within limestone wall-rocks, the host limestone has been partially replaced for up to several metres on either side of the vein by mineralising solutions, creating extensive bodies of mineralisation known as 'flats'.

A distinctive feature of this orefield is the marked zonal distribution of some of the minerals. A central zone, which includes much of Alston Moor, Weardale and parts of Teesdale, in which fluorite is extremely abundant, is surrounded by an outer zone in which barium minerals, including baryte and witherite, predominate. It was this zonation that first invited speculation on the presence of a concealed granitic body at depth and of its likely role in the formation of the ore deposits. The granite was proved in the Rookhope Borehole drilled in 1960-61. Although the granite was shown to be older than the Carboniferous rocks, its high heat flow is believed to have driven the convective flow of the mineralising fluids that created the area's veins.

Cow Green Mine. Miners working underground in a stope in 1949. The baryte vein is clearly seen in the roof
© Friends of Killhope Archive

Much of Teesdale lies close to the southern margins of the fluorite zone. Lead has been worked from numerous mines in the Dale, the largest of which lie north and north-west of Middleton. Small amounts of zinc ores were extracted locally and prospecting for this metal was pursued around Ettersgill [NY89052910] during World War Two. Attempts to rework old Teesdale lead mines for fluorspar yielded only modest amounts. By contrast, large tonnages of barytes were extracted from mines at Cow Green [NY81053053] and Closehouse [NY85002260], the latter of which closed in the 1990s.

Coldberry Gutter, looking west towards the upper part of the Dale. The prominent rock to the left of the hammer is a fine exposure of the Cleveland-Armarthwaite Dyke. Traditionally regarded as a large lead mining hush, the gutter is now thought to be a glacial meltwater channel, excavated along a major fault and mineral vein.
© Brian Young

Mining has left an indelible mark on Upper Teesdale with spoil heaps, ruined buildings and opencast workings, including 'hushes', locally conspicuous. 'Hushes' are wide trench-like opencast workings, traditionally regarded as an early form of hydraulic mining, excavated by the repeated release of torrents of water from specially created reservoirs. However, critical examination of many hushes suggests that they are more likely to have been created by manual excavation followed by flushing with water released from such dams. Notable areas of long abandoned mining in the Dale, perhaps of some antiquity, include the Grasshill Mines in the Harwood valley [NY82103570], the Pike Law Mines on Newbiggin Common [NY90103200] and the extensive old workings around Coldberry at the head of the Hudeshope valley [NY94402930]. One of the Dale's most conspicuous landmarks, the huge trench-like Coldberry Gutter that breaches the watershed between the Bow Lee and Hudeshope valleys [NY92702890 – NY93902910], has traditionally been regarded as a particularly large hush. However, it has recently been suggested that the 'Gutter' may be a glacial meltwater channel with only minor modifications due to mining.

Much of Middleton-in-Teesdale was remodelled in the nineteenth century by the London Lead Company, the main mining company, whose headquarters were at Middleton House [NY9450 2580], the prominent building that dominates the western outskirts of the village.

Communities of (Calaminarian) plants, adapted to thrive on soils associated with heavy metal deposits are discussed elsewhere in this book.

Geological maps

Teesdale is covered by British Geological Survey (BGS) 1:50 000 and 1:63 360 scale sheets 25 (Alston), 31 (Brough-under-Stainmore) and 32 (Barnard Castle) with 1:25 000 scale coverage for part of the Dale on Sheet NY82 (Middleton-in-Teesdale).

Further reading

The reader wishing to explore any aspect of the Dale's geology in greater depth may find the following publications useful. References to even greater detailed descriptions in other technical publications are given in most of these.

Burgess, I C and Holliday, D W, 1979, *Geology of the country around Brough-under-Stainmore*, Memoir of the Geological Survey of Great Britain, England and Wales, Sheet 31. HMSO, London.

Dunham, K C, 1990, Geology of the Northern Pennine Orefield (2nd edition); Volume 1 Tyne to Stainmore. *Economic Memoir of the British Geological Survey*, England and Wales.HMSO, London

Evans, D J A(Editor), 2017, *The Quaternary Landscape history of Teesdale and the North Pennines. – Field Guide*, Quaternary Research Association, London.

Forbes, I, Young, B, Crossley, C And Hehir, L, 2003. *The lead mining landscape of the North Pennines Area of Outstanding Natural Beauty*, Durham County Council, Durham.

Johnson, G A L, 1995, Robson's Geology of North east England (Second edition), *Transactions of the Natural History Society of Northumbria* Vol. 56, Part 5, pp226-391.

Johnson, G A L, and Dunham, K C, 1963, The geology of Moorhouse, *Monograph of the Nature Conservancy*. HMSO, London.

Mills, D A C and Hull, J H, 1976, Geology of the country around Barnard Castle, *Memoir of the Geological Survey of Great Britain*. HMSO, London.

North Pennines AONB Partnership (E Pickett), 2011, *Reading the rocks: Exploring the geology and landscape of the North Pennines*, North Pennines AONB Partnership, Stanhope.

Scrutton, C T (Editor), 2004, *Northumbrian Rocks and Landscape* (Second edition), Yorkshire Geological Society. Leeds.

Stone, P, Millward, D, Young, B, Merritt, J W, Clarke, S M, Mccormac, M and Lawrence, D J D, 2010, *British Regional Geology: Northern England* (Fifth edition), British Geological Survey, Keyworth, Nottingham.

Symes, R F and Young, B, 2008, *Minerals of Northern England*, NMS Enterprises, National Museums of Scotland, Edinburgh.

Chapter 4

Geomorphology and Quaternary glacial legacy

by David J A Evans

Introduction

The last 2.6 million years of earth history (the Quaternary Period) is characterised by large volumes of global ice relative to previous geological periods and is the culmination of a long term cooling trend that began some 55 million ago. The extent of ice has varied in an oscillatory fashion so that the Quaternary Period is characterised by two dominant climate extremes called glacials and interglacials. However, the climate is never stable, oscillating instead dynamically from one extreme state to the other and necessitating the use of the terms stadial and interstadial to refer to phases of relative cold and warmth during glacial stages.

Many physiographic details of the North Pennines relate specifically to the lithological and structural control of the underlying bedrock, whose denudation and incision has resulted in conspicuous stepped hillslope profiles and tableland type topographic features. Additionally, the area contains some remarkable relict channels and underfit valleys (those now hosting streams too small to have been capable of cutting them), which are developed respectively on valley sides and across lower lying, undulatory to hummocky topography; such valleys are either of a glacial meltwater origin or relate to more complex and longer timescale combined fluvial and glacial origin (Evans 2017). The longer timescale drainage features date to fluvial processes that may have operated long before the onset of the Ice Age or the Quaternary Period.

Glaciation is manifest in the landscapes of Teesdale and the North Pennines in the form of erosional features cut directly by the ice or by its meltwater and more obviously in the form of glacigenic drift. Drift is a term used to describe surface materials that are clearly related to former ice action and includes glacifluvial sands and gravels (meltwater deposits) and tills (poorly sorted sediments plastered on the landscape by glacier ice). Early geologists referred to tills as 'boulder clays', a term that unfortunately still persists despite being entirely inappropriate due to the fact that tills are hardly ever composed only of boulders and clay.

Bedrock controls on physiography and Quaternary deposits

The physiography of the North Pennines, and Teesdale in particular, is dictated by the fabric of the bedrock geology, which gives rise to an eastward-dipping dissected plateau, upon which it is thought that early eastward-draining river networks were developed (Mills & Hull 1976). The strong geomorphological inheritance of the underlying bedrock structure and lithology is exemplified by the sub-horizontal valley-side benches and flat-topped mountain summits (or mesas and buttes), which reflect the predominantly flat-lying to shallow dipping strata of the Carboniferous sandstones, millstone grits, limestones and coal measures.

The tableland or mesa and butte topographic features at the highest elevations along the North Pennine upland chain have developed into extensive mountain summit blockfields, interpreted as the products of *in situ* frost-shattering. The blockfield on Cross Fell (Mitchell & Huddart 2002) and adjacent hilltops has been central to long standing debates on the former existence of nunataks above the British-Irish Ice Sheet (Dwerryhouse 1902; Raistrick 1931). Small areas of blockfield also exist on the summits of Little Fell, Mickle Fell, Long Crag and Bink Moss to the south of the River Tees and Middleton Common, Monk's Moor and Eggleston Common to the north. The alternative interpretation of these blockfields (Trotter 1929) was that they had survived beneath a cover of thin and passive glacier ice. More recently, Trotter's idea has been substantiated and the vertical transition from upper drift limits to blockfield is interpreted as marking a thermal boundary in formerly extensive ice sheets; this involves the occurrence of warm ice in valleys where it is thickest and cold ice on surrounding summits where it is thinnest and dynamically sluggish or even inert.

Quaternary deposits that overlie this predominantly stepped bedrock topography thicken in valley bottoms in a range of glacial landforms but thin rapidly upslope above the middle Tees valley and its tributaries to form

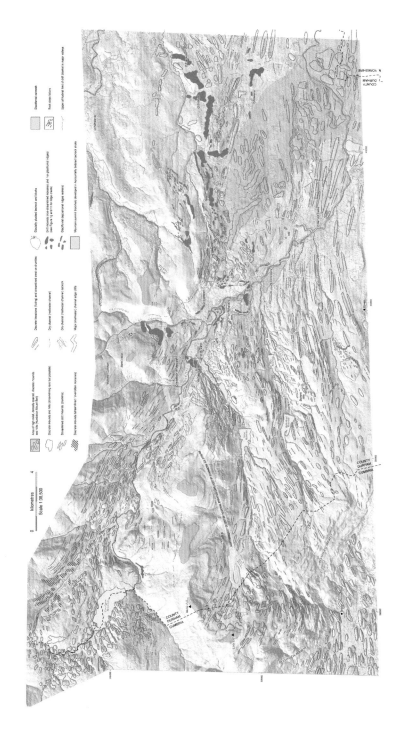

Figure 1: Glacial geomorphology of Teesdale and adjacent areas mapped on a digital elevation model derived from NEXTMap imagery (courtesy of NERC via the Earth Observation Data Centre).

a clear drift limit; above this limit the Quaternary deposits form an often patchy veneer through which bedrock structure is clearly visible (Figure 1; Evans 2017). Mapped over the region as 'boulder clay' with valley floor pockets of 'glacial sand and gravel' (Mills & Hull 1976), this Quaternary cover thins also towards the valley heads of Upper Teesdale, Lunedale, Baldersdale and Deepdale, in the direction of the NW–SE trending ridge of the North Pennines mountain chain. This mountain chain (600-890 m) is punctuated by passes to the north and south of the Mickle Fell/Little Fell summit ridge, the latter forming one of several cols that feed into the drainage basins of Lunedale, Baldersdale and Deepdale; the glacially streamlined, relatively lower elevation topography of this terrain is collectively named the Stainmore Gap, after the pass (Stainmore Common/Cotherstone Moor) that crosses the North Pennines between the higher summit massifs of the Durham and Yorkshire dales.

Glacierisation of the North Pennines

Contrary to many media-based, popularised views of the ice age, ice sheets do not march southwards from the Arctic to engulf mid-latitude regions like Northern England when colder conditions prevail. Instead it is the upland surfaces, like the Pennines themselves, which spawn glaciers and ice caps, simply because they are at relatively high altitude, where colder environmental conditions will cause the accumulation of snow first. The operation of a North Pennines independent ice dispersal centre during glaciations was first proposed by Dakyns *et al.* (1891), Dwerryhouse (1902) and Raistrick (1931). They envisaged that the ice built up in the easterly-facing

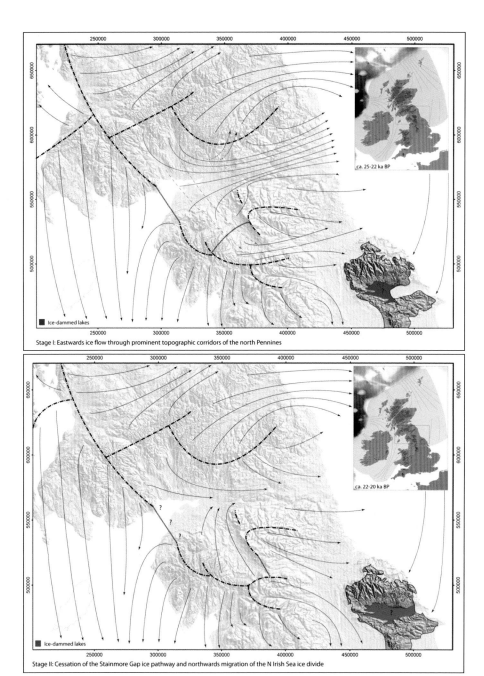

Figure 2: Time slices in the palaeoglaciological reconstruction of the British-Irish Ice Sheet of northern England and southern Scotland (modified from Livingstone *et al.* 2012), showing changes in ice divides and dispersal centres during the last glaciation and their influence on ice flow patterns.

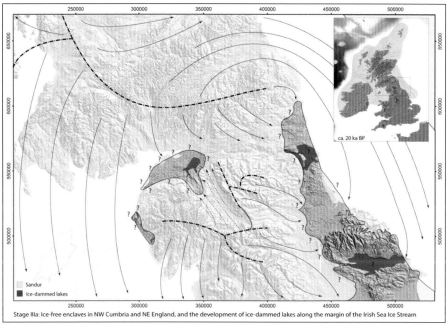

Stage IIIa: Ice-free enclaves in NW Cumbria and NE England, and the development of ice-dammed lakes along the margin of the Irish Sea Ice Stream

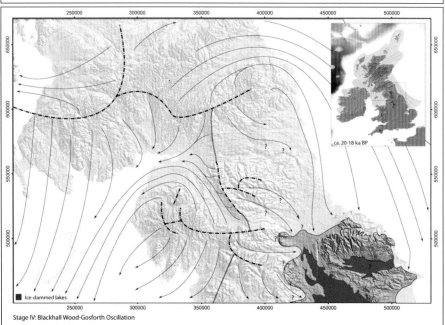

Stage IV: Blackhall Wood-Gosforth Oscillation

65

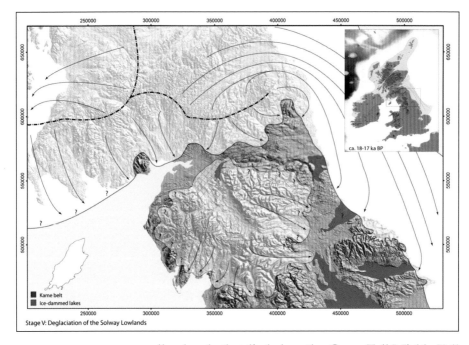

valley heads that lie below the Cross Fell-Mickle Fell summit ridge, resulting in northerly and easterly flowing valley glaciers in the Tyne, Wear and Tees catchments. Regional ice flowing from Scotland then flowed around this partially ice-covered upland, creating major ice streams in the Tyne Gap and Vale of Eden/Stainmore Gap. This pattern of ice flow is one that persists in modern reconstructions (Figure 2) but some significant details have been refined, as detailed below.

The notion that palaeonunataks lay above these various fast-flowing ice masses was based on the assumption that the summit blockfields, such as Cross Fell, required long periods of freeze-thaw weathering to develop and hence must have lain above the ice during glaciation. We now understand that not only can blockfield form quickly (ie. in postglacial time) but it can also survive beneath the cold-based inert ice that would have been typical of such upland settings during glaciation; indeed glacierisation started on these uplands. So it is now conventional, as introduced above, to interpret the transition between upper drift limits and blockfield as thermal boundaries in ice sheets.

So instead of lying above the ice sheets, the Pennine uplands were one of the spawning grounds for them. This was first appreciated climatologically in the 1950s' research of Gordon Manley, who used the North Pennines to identify important relationships between snowfall accumulation and physiography, noting the tendency for plateaux in particular to be the seeding grounds of ice caps and hence to play a critical role in the early stages of glacierisation during cold stages of the Quaternary Period. This plateau-icefield style of initial glacierisation creates a particular landform imprint, but one that is often overrun and hence heavily modified by more extensive ice sheet growth as a glaciation progresses. In terms of geomorphological change in terrains like the North Pennines, the highest plateaux are likely to have been occupied by ice for the longest cumulative period of time throughout the Quaternary Period, because most of that Period of 2.6 million years has been characterised by an Earth surface with an intermediate style of glacier coverage; so the planet has for most of the Ice Age been in a state of glacierisation that lies somewhere between full glacial maxima (extensive ice sheets) and interglacial minima (like the present day). This concept is termed 'average' glacial conditions and these are the most effective in terms of longer term landscape change because they dominate for most of the time.

In order to understand the range of possible plateau

icefield glacial configurations on the North Pennines, Evans and Jamieson (2017) used a numerical glacier model driven by the palaeoclimate data from the Greenland ice core record. This record covers the period that includes the Younger Dryas Stadial of 12,900–11,700 years ago, when mountain glaciers re-occupied the British Isles after having largely disappeared at the end of the last glaciation. This phase of glacierisation is significant because it is regarded globally as the likely average glacial condition for the Quaternary Period. The evidence for two small glaciers of possible Younger Dryas age have been identified in Upper Teesdale (see below), but one, Tarn Rigg (445 m), is contentious and the other, High Cup Plain (580 m), is likely an underestimate of plateau ice cover. The altitudes of both sites can however be used to drive the numerical model, because they can be used as upper and lower estimates of the glacier equilibrium line altitude

Figure 3 Maximum Younger Dryas ice extent (left) and the duration of ice margin stabilisation (right) for two model scenarios including the likely ELA of 580 m (top) and a lower ELA of 445 m (bottom). From Evans and Jamieson (2017).

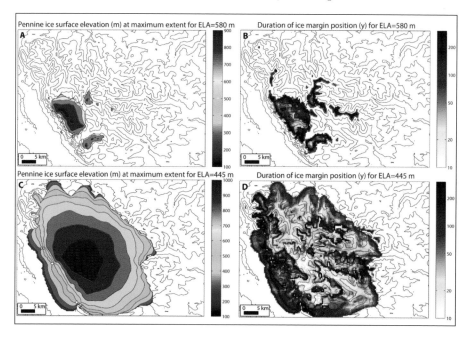

(ELA = the altitude at which a glacier can exist, because it marks the altitude at which inputs of snow and ice equal outputs due to melting). The model output for the 580 m ELA simulation (Figure 3A) reveals that the Younger Dryas palaeo-temperatures are sufficient to build a small but reasonably stable plateau icefield in the North Pennines and the ice reaches the location of the proposed High Cup Plain glacier. The model also shows the locations likely to be characterised by the build-up of drift (moraines) due to the duration of ice-marginal stability (Figure 3B). The 445 m ELA experiment (Figures 3C & 3D) creates far more extensive ice, with the Teesdale ice reaching beyond Barnard Castle at its maximum and hence an ice cover that is too large to align with field evidence for potential Younger Dryas glacier ice. It does, however, show that under a more extreme glacial climate the regional ice cover develops initially from plateau dispersal centres. This plateau icefield style of glacierisation was subsumed only during full ice sheet conditions by easterly-draining ice streams of an ice sheet that extended as far south as North Norfolk in the east and the Isles of Scilly in the west.

Once coalescent, all the ice masses that were expanding from their various upland dispersal centres (eg. North Pennines, Lake District, Southern Uplands, Scottish Highlands) submerged the landscape and evolved in glacierisation style from topographically-confined flow to unconfined full ice sheet flow. The latter was characterised by significant ice flow reversals over the North Pennines in particular (Figure 2). We now understand ice sheets to be extremely dynamic systems in which flow directions, particularly those related to ice streams, switch in response to changes in ice sheet thickness and dispersal centre locations. In the North Pennines the extent of the regional ice (derived from Scotland) and the persistence of plateau-centred local ice throughout glaciation was identified by the mapping of erratics (Johnson & Dunham 1963; Vincent 1969; Taylor *et al.* 1971; Francis 1974; Lunn 1995a, b, 2004). This showed that only the higher plateau of Cross Fell and Cold Fell contained no westerly-derived regional erratics and hence it generated independent ice that flowed radially but most strongly eastwards down Teesdale (Figure 4). This easterly flow was a result of the Pennine ice being forced to flow with the stronger Scottish-derived regional ice during the ice sheet maximum phase while at the same time still excluding it from the highest Pennine plateau.

Glacial geomorphology of Teesdale

In addition to the distribution of erratics, the most significant landform evidence for former ice sheet flow patterns comes from streamlined drift mounds, often composed entirely of till and called drumlins and flutings (Figures 1 and 5). Although the exact origins of these features are debated, it is accepted that they record the streamlining of deformable and erodible materials by a glacier as it flows over its bed. Where little deformable material (sediment) is available, the ice can produce similarly streamlined forms by dragging debris over the bedrock and eroding it to produce features called whalebacks or rock drumlins. As the long axes of these streamlined forms are aligned with former glacier flow, it is easy to reconstruct the ice flow dynamics. Additionally, changes in ice flow direction over time can result in the overprinting of streamlined forms and we

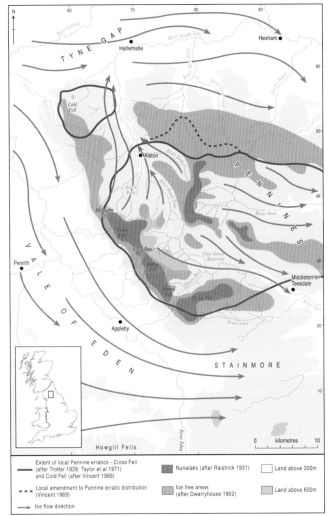

Figure 4: Map of Upper Teesdale and adjacent areas showing the former ice flow directions depicted by Dwerryhouse (1902) at a relatively early stage of ice flow up the Vale of Eden from Scotland. Note the radial flow of the Pennine-centred ice from the Cross Fell plateau and the deflection of easterly flowing Tyne Gap and Stainmore Gap ice streams around this ice. Also shown are the proposed nunataks of the north Pennines from Dwerryhouse (1902) and Raistrick (1931), features now interpreted as the levels of thermal regime changes in the overlying ice sheet. Red lines demarcate the limit of regional, western-derived erratics and thereby outline areas characterised by Pennine erratics only (after Trotter 1929; Vincent 1969; Taylor et al. 1971).

have such evidence recorded in the patterns of alignment and overprinting in the drumlins and flutings of Teesdale and adjacent areas.

The drumlins and flutings display some relatively high elongation ratios (up to 13.75) and a relief of up to 20 m. A restricted number of valley floor exposures reveal multiple till sequences up to 10 m thick, but elsewhere many streamlined features merely constitute discrete lineations that are likely controlled by underlying bedrock structure, especially on the northern slopes of Upper Teesdale and on the higher terrain of the Stainmore Gap. Drumlinoid drift tails have also been developed on the interfluves of the tributaries to the upper River Tees where older recessional lateral moraines (see below) likely have been glacially overridden. Abnormally large drumlinised mounds (15-20 m relief) but with low elongation ratios (2.25 - 3.0) occur on the floor of Upper Teesdale, at Holwick. These streamlined landforms show that regional ice sheet flow was dominated by the easterly flowing Tyne Gap and Stainmore Gap ice streams. The limit of the Teesdale ice, or more specifically its suture zone with the Stainmore ice stream, was first identified by Dwerryhouse (1902) using the distribution of regional erratics. Teesdale ice was deflected significantly northwards downstream of Middleton-in-Teesdale to flow into the drainage of the Gaunless Valley, as determined by the distribution of Shap granites delivered by the Stainmore ice stream (Figure 1).

In the Upper Teesdale catchment, Mitchell (2007) used the cross-cutting relationships of the drumlins in the Moor House/Cow Green area to show that changes in ice flow direction took place also in the Pennine-centred ice, likely when it was a smaller plateau-based ice mass. An early southerly ice flow appears to have been driven by an west-east aligned ice divide but this was replaced by an easterly to southeasterly ice flow when the ice divide migrated westwards. Drumlins like this, which are indicative of significant subglacial sedimentation and deformation (thick drift), are unusual in upland settings such as the upper Tees catchment. So why is there so much drift in Upper Teesdale?

Figure 5: Teesdale drumlins: a) west of Cow Green Reservoir; b) Forest-in-Teesdale; c) Seats Hill, Holwick; and d) multiple tills in a drumlin at Stack Holme, Lunedale
© D J A Evans

To answer this we return to our concept of 'average' glacial conditions. The summit ice of plateau icefields, because it is both thin and a centre of dispersal, and hence of low flow velocity, is predominantly geomorphologically inert or protective. As a result the maximum erosional and depositional capacity of such systems is concentrated in surrounding, lower elevation valley heads where strain heating is induced by increased flow velocities. This gives rise to a concentration of depositional landforms not on the plateaux but on the lower surrounding terrain. Based upon our numerical modelling (Figure 3) we can assume quite confidently that for most of the last glacial cycle the short occupancy time of mountain icefields was capable of producing only subtle erosional and depositional imprints and that the most substantial depositional products of repeat glaciations should lie in this intermediate zone at the plateau base. Using our knowledge of debris transport pathways through glaciers, we can predict that over time an ice mass will advect material towards its margin. Hence, each ice margin will be marked by a marginal-thickening wedge of subglacial sediment, the volume of which is dictated by the residence time of the ice (Figure 3). So it is highly likely that the large volume of glacigenic debris represented by the Cow Green drumlins marks the location of plateau icefield marginal moraines constructed during average glacial conditions and then subsumed by thick erosive ice during phases of more extensive, regional ice flow activity.

Other, non-streamlined, drift mounds in Teesdale are more difficult to interpret in terms of former glacial processes. Some contain substantial glacitectonic bedrock rafts (Figure 6a), as demonstrated by reports on a rare extensive exposure temporarily made available at an opencast coal mine near Tow Law (Mills 1976). Although outside Teesdale, this exposure through hillocks (Figure 6b) clearly illustrates the importance of bedrock dislocation and glacitectonic raft development in the Carboniferous strata of the region. In the Upper Teesdale catchment, further impressive examples are the Bullman Hills and Lambgreen Hills (Lunn 1995a, b) which are huge blocks of Great Limestone displaced from the Cross Fell summit and carried northwards by ice dispersing radially on the Cross Fell plateau (Figure 6c). Some drift mounds appear to be overridden moraines because their plan form resembles that of latero-frontal moraines in narrow valley settings but their surfaces are faintly fluted or streamlined. An excellent example occurs on the floor of Harwood Beck near Low End (Figure 7a), which likely demarcates the limits of plateau-based ice during average glacial conditions, later streamlined by easterly flowing regional ice streams.

Examples of unaltered latero-frontal moraines or arcuate, valley floor drift assemblages are recognisable throughout Teesdale. The most obvious latero-frontal moraines occur near Cronkley Scar, where they demarcate the margins of a valley-confined glacier lobe at the later stages of deglaciation (Figure 7b). A further substantial assemblage of drift mounds forms an arcuate loop across the main Teesdale valley between the villages of Romaldkirk and Cotherstone, the largest of which is a wide cross-valley ridge, named locally the Gueswick Hills and mapped as morainic drift by Mills and Hull (1976). The Gueswick Hills can be traced onto the west and east slopes of Teesdale as discontinuous linear ridges (Figure 8); those on the east slopes below High Shipley ascend diagonally upslope to a more extensive assemblage of mounds in the area around Folly Head and Windy Hill and those on the west bank form an arc that extends up stream to join patchy drift mounds around Romaldkirk. Immediately to the northwest of the Gueswick Moraine, a number of discrete, non-streamlined drift mounds are similarly interpreted as glacier marginal deposits. Although exposures are rare, the occurrence of these mounds on valley sides and interfluves and across valley floors strongly suggests that they are glacigenic. The largest of these mound types are in Eggleston Burn and includes a dissected cross valley ridge and an expanse of hummocks and ridges on the interfluve with the main Teesdale valley above Froggerthwaite, the latter interpreted as 'ablation moraine' by Mills and Hull (1976). Their orientation, as well as their association with lateral meltwater channels on the adjacent higher slopes, suggests that these mounds (collectively hereby termed the Froggerthwaite Moraine; Figure 8) were deposited at the margin of topographically confined ice in Teesdale when it back-filled Eggleston Burn during overall ice sheet recession. Finally, an area of substantial

Figure 6: Glacitectonic thrust masses of bedrock: a) idealized sketch of the formation of a glacitectonised raft (modified from Evans & Benn 2010); b) the Sunniside and Broom Hill interfluve glacitectonic rafts, near Tow Law, County Durham, showing repetition of strata after Mills (1974) and Moore (1994); c) view within and across the Bullman Hills from the southwest, showing the flat-topped nature of the mounds and the surface outcrops of the Great Limestone that comprises the core of the landform assemblage.
Photography © D J A Evans

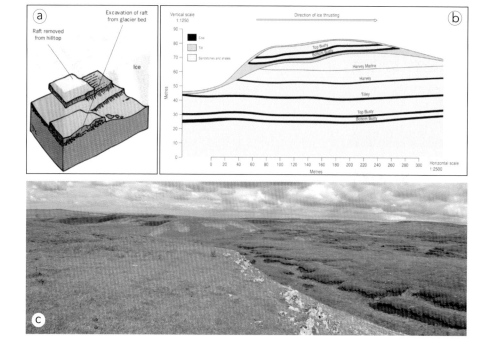

drift mounds occurs around the area of Lonton and Laithkirk, at the junction of Lunedale and Teesdale. These features are closely associated with densely spaced and deeply incised lateral meltwater channels that demarcate the receding margins and former coalescence zone of Teesdale and Lunedale ice lobes (see below). Each of these landform assemblages marks a separate stage in the recession of ice in Teesdale, some of which are readvances (Figure 8b; Evans 2017).

Glacifluvial landforms and deposits are well represented in the North Pennines and comprise meltwater channels and eskers and kames (Figure 1). A number of elongate ridges and associated mounds and benches can be confidently ascribed to glacifluvial depositional processes because they are composed of

Figure 7: Latero-frontal moraines; a) large drift ridges of Harwood Beck viewed from the west. Valley side ridges descend diagonally down slope towards valley floor ridges. The largest valley floor ridge is that in the middle distance, which crosses the valley near Low End. This feature appears to have been overridden by glacier ice during the last glaciation; b) inset sequence of linear ridges (lateral moraines) below Widdy Bank in Upper Teesdale, documenting the recession of topographically confined ice into the Cow Green area.
© D J A Evans

sands and gravels (cf. Mills and Hull 1976). Other features in which there are no sedimentary exposures have also been interpreted as glacifluvial in origin based upon their morphology and general context or relationships with other landforms. The most extensive spread of glacifluvial deposits occurs in undulatory and weakly pitted benches on the margins of the River Tees valley floor located between Middleton-in-Teesdale and Romaldkirk. A number of discontinuous, elongate ridges occur on the surfaces of these benches, as well as further up valley, where they lie in isolation on the River Tees floodplain between Middleton-in-Teesdale and Bowlees. These features are interpreted as eskers, the internal sediments of which are exposed in small pits at Hayberries, near Romaldkirk (Figure 9a). Exposures through the glacifluvial deposits of the benches also occur near Mickleton (poorly-sorted, boulder to cobble gravels) and west of Eggleston Hall (horizontally bedded gravels and sands overlying till), indicative of kame terrace origins. Two further spreads of glacifluvial outwash exist beyond the Gueswick Hills Moraine, their apexes emerging from substantial meltwater channels. An unusual glacifluvial assemblage is the Woolly Hills, which forms a triangular-shaped assemblage of sharp-crested ridges and chaotic high relief hummocks and straddles the watershed separating the Hindon Beck (Gaunless) and Woolly Gill (Spurlswood Beck) drainage basins, clearly recording former subglacial or englacial meltwater flow that crossed normal fluvial drainage basins. Given the close proximity of this elongate assemblage of glacifluvial landforms to the suture zone of regional (Stainmore) ice and Pennine (Teesdale) ice, as defined by the northernmost extent of regional erratics (Figures 1 & 8), it is likely that it represents

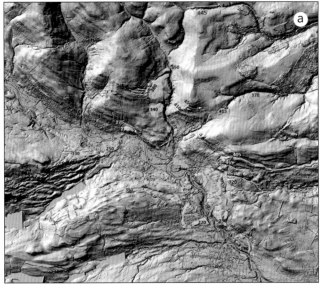

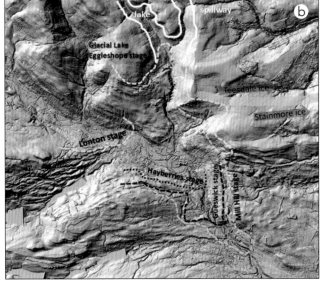

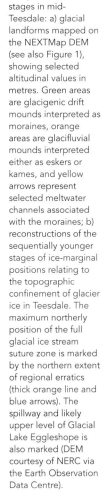

Figure 8: The glacial features and interpreted glacial stages in mid-Teesdale: a) glacial landforms mapped on the NEXTMap DEM (see also Figure 1), showing selected altitudinal values in metres. Green areas are glacigenic drift mounds interpreted as moraines, orange areas are glacifluvial mounds interpreted either as eskers or kames, and yellow arrows represent selected meltwater channels associated with the moraines; b) reconstructions of the sequentially younger stages of ice-marginal positions relating to the topographic confinement of glacier ice in Teesdale. The maximum northerly position of the full glacial ice stream suture zone is marked by the northern extent of regional erratics (thick orange line and blue arrows). The spillway and likely upper level of Glacial Lake Eggleshope is also marked (DEM courtesy of NERC via the Earth Observation Data Centre).

deposition in the suture zone of the two ice flow units when meltwater was draining preferentially along the supraglacial 'valley' and associated englacial and subglacial drainage network created at the point of coalescence (Evans 2017).

Meltwater erosional features are particularly well developed around Teesdale. A number of possible preglacial or consequent valleys may have been re-occupied by glacial meltwater, thereby explaining their partial drift infill and locally prominent cliff margins. Clusters of spectacular dry valleys and channels of unequivocal deglacial meltwater origin occur along valley margins and hence are associated with ice-marginal or lateral meltwater drainage and sub-marginal drainage or chutes (Dyke 1993; Syverson & Mickelson 2009). A prominent series of meltwater channels cut through and descend from the Butterknowle/Copley/Wigglesworth fault scarp into Langleydale. These meltwater channels descend diagonally from the fault scarp and record lateral meltwater incision at the margin of glacier ice downwasting from the scarp top. Early lateral meltwater incision at the margins of this ice was concentred on Arn Gill, which drains into the River Gaunless drainage basin to the north of the fault scarp summit and can be traced back to prominent channels cut into the bedrock slopes above Eggleston and Folly Head. Once the ice margin had downwasted below the fault scarp summits of Peatmoor Crag and Cragg Top/Penny Hill, lateral meltwater began draining southeastwards and into the Langleydale drainage basin. At later stages of ice recession, meltwater continued to be diverted into the floor of Langleydale via substantial bedrock gorges to the east of Folly Head, specifically at Pallet Crag Gill and Howe Gill, thereby initiating the later stages of incision of the drift infill.

The large volume of meltwater that was diverted into the Arn Gill/Gaunless drainage basin and then Langleydale is unusual in that glacier ice lay over significantly lower topography to the south, especially over Teesdale, and therefore meltwater had to be flowing at high levels within the ice in order for it to be delivered into the easterly draining valleys. Ice-marginal or lateral meltwater drainage would have been capable of such a flow pattern and indeed lateral meltwater channels exist on the southern slopes of Monk's Moor and also across the Hett Dyke on the southeastern corner of Egglestone Common (Figure 8), where they are responsible for the creation of the bedrock ridges called Knotts. The uppermost channel on Monk's Moor descends from around 500 m to 410 m, after turning to flow up valley around the Froggerthwaite Moraine like all the inset meltwater channels on this slope (Figure 8). On the east valley side, the uppermost channel at Knotts is at 450 m. In order to cut channels at isolated locations at such high altitudes on both sides of the Egglestone Burn, valley water flow would have to be ice-directed and hence is further evidence, in addition to the Froggerthwaite Moraine, that a lobe of Lunedale ice in Teesdale backfilled the lower half of the valley. Indeed this pattern of drainage channel development was regarded by Mills and Hull (1976) as evidence for glacial lake spillways, whereby the upper Egglestone Burn valley was dammed by ice in Teesdale to form a lake (called Glacial Lake Eggleshope). This lake was also proposed by Dwerryhouse (1902), who identified the substantial dry gorge of Sharnberry Gill, which cuts across the eastern watershed of the valley at an altitude of 445 m, as the northern lake spillway. This spillway carried the lake waters into Euden Beck and ultimately to the River Wear drainage basin but was terminated as an outlet once the lower channels at Knotts were incised. A flat-floored dry channel located at 415 m at the head of Spurlswood Gill indicates that spillway waters entered the Wear drainage basin via that route after Sharnberry Gill ceased to operate. This would have required ice to be occupying the Blackton Head area but it is likely that marginal meltwater was draining along the south slopes of Grey Carrs to enter the Redmire Gill channel at 405 m at around the same time, when the Mill Hill Moraine was being constructed (Figure 8). The final drainage of Glacial Lake Eggleshope was likely subglacial, beneath the thinning ice lobe occupying Teesdale, as evidenced by a small esker remnant inside the Froggerthwaite Moraine. The lack of glacilacustrine deposits suggests that it was a short-lived lake, but the size of the Froggerthwaite Moraine is consistent with a substantial stillstand and/or readvance of the Teesdale valley ice and so an alternative explanation for sparse lake sediments is that the lake drained frequently, potentially creating jökulhlaups or glacier floods that could at least partially explain the significant erosion of the gorges below Redmire Gill and Goose Tarn Beck and even have contributed to the deep incision of Arn Gill and the Gaunless valley.

A further spectacular assemblage of meltwater channels has been developed on the slopes of Lunedale (Figure 8 and 9b, c), documenting the recession of the Lunedale valley glacier once it had become topographically confined by the valley; hence the Stainmore Gap ice stream, of which the ice in Lundedale was part, had ceased to operate as a regional flow unit. The development of clusters of inset meltwater channels such as this, in locations that clearly relate to the more advanced stages of ice sheet deglaciation, has been identified not only on the nearby Pennine Escarpment by Arthurton and Wadge (1981),

Greenwood *et al.* (2007) and Livingstone *et al.* (2010) but also in Strathallan, Perthshire by Evans *et al.* (2017), who regard this as a geomorphic signature of a significant change in meltwater drainage patterns, likely related to the temporary development of cold-based or polythermal ice conditions, the regional palaeoglaciological implications of which are still to be elucidated.

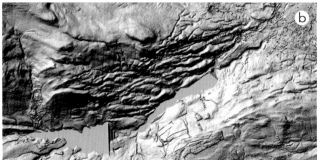

Figure 9: Examples of glacifluvial landforms of Teesdale: a) view westwards along the Mickleton-Egglestone glacifluvial terrace directly west of the Hayberries esker complex; b) NEXTMap DEM extract of the glacial landforms of lower Lunedale, showing the en echelon arrangement of lateral meltwater channels and their relationship with the Lonton Moraine and meltwater channels associated with former Teesdale ice. Also visible are streamlined mounds (drumlins) around which channels have been incised; c) one of the most prominent of the lateral meltwater channels on the north side of Lunedale, below Kirkcarrion. Photography by D J A Evans and DEM courtesy of NERC via the Earth Observation Data Centre.

As discussed above, the most recent glacigenic imprint in the North Pennines has previously been proposed to be of Younger Dryas Stadial age (12,900-11,700 years ago), during which small niche or proto-cirque glaciers where thought to have developed in High Cup Plain (Manley 1961) and below Cronkley Scar (Wilson & Clark 1995). Like other areas that lay at the threshold of glacierisation during the Younger Dryas, the North Pennines contain debris mounds in potential ice accumulation basins or hillside niches that have been variably interpreted as glacial (moraines), periglacial (protalus ramparts) or rock slope failures. Mitchell (1991), reviewing earlier proposals for small glaciers based upon such features (Rowell & Turner 1952; Manley 1961), proposed that five sites in the western Pennines were of glacial origin and hence the ELA during the Younger Dryas was between 313-612 m. Wilson and Clark's (1995) re-assessment of the debris assemblage at Tarn Rigg, below Cronkley Scar, as an end moraine rather than a lateral moraine as proposed by Dwerryhouse (1902), indicates a Younger Dryas ELA in Upper Teesdale of 445 m. The High Cup Plain landforms, if they are of glacial origin and are Younger Dryas in age, indicate an ELA of 580 m. Although the ELAs of both the proposed Tarn Rigg and High Cup Plain palaeo-glaciers lie within Mitchell's (1991) altitude range for Younger Dryas glaciation in the adjacent western Pennines, an ELA difference of 135 m between the two sites over such a short distance and within the confines of Upper Teesdale is problematic in terms glacier-climate reconstructions. Indeed, the low elevation of Tarn Rigg is at odds with the easterly rise in ELAs across the western Pennines reported by Mitchell (1991). As we saw above

(Figure 3), the use of such a low ELA altitude in numerical glacier modelling produces an abnormally large Younger Dryas icefield and so the glacier cover in Upper Teesdale during this period was more likely to have been a thin plateau icefield with small outlet lobes such as that on High Cup Plain.

References

Arthurton, R S. and Wadge, A J, 1981, Geology of the country around Penrith, *Memoir of the Geological Survey of Great Britain.*

Benn, D I and Evans, D J A, 2010, *Glaciers and Glaciation.* Hodder Education, London.

Dakyns, J R, Tiddeman, R H, Russell, R, Clough, C T and Strahan, A, 1891, The geology of the country around Mallerstang with parts of Wensleydale, Swaledale and Arkendale. Sheet 97NW Memoir of the Geological Survey of Great Britain HMSO, London.

Dwerryhouse, A R, 1902, The glaciation of Teesdale, Weardale, and the Tyne valley, and their tributary valleys. *Quarterly Journal of the Geological Society of London* **58**, pp572-608.

Dyke, A S, 1993, Landscapes of cold-centred Late Wisconsin ice caps, Arctic Canada, *Progress in Physical Geography* **17**, pp223-247.

Evans, D J A, 2017 (ed.), *The Quaternary Landscape History of Teesdale and the North Pennines — Field Guide.* Quaternary Research Association, London.

Evans, D J A and Jamieson, S S R, 2017, 'The North Pennines climate and glacierisation: plateau icefields and the concept of average glacial conditions', in Evans D J A (ed.), *The Quaternary Landscape History of Teesdale and the North Pennines — Field Guide.* Quaternary Research Association, London, pp68-75.

Evans, D J A, Hughes, A L C, Hansom, J D and Roberts, D H, 2017, Scottish Landform Examples 43: Glacifluvial landforms of Strathallan, Perthshire. *Scottish Geographical Journal* **133**, pp42-53.

Francis, E A, 1974, 'Quaternary', in Hickling, G (ed.), 'The Geology of Durham County', *Transactions of the Natural History Society of Northumberland, Durham and Newcastle upon Tyne* **41**, pp134-153.

Greenwood, S L, Clark, C D and Hughes, A L C, 2007, 'Formalising an inversion methodology for reconstructing ice-sheet retreat patterns from meltwater channels: application to the British Ice Sheet', *Journal of Quaternary Science* **22**, pp637-645.

Johnson, G A L and Dunham, K C, 1963, 'The geology of Moorhouse', *Monograph of the Nature Conservancy*.

Livingstone, S J, Evans, D J A, Ó Cofaigh, C and Hopkins, J, 2010, 'The Brampton Kame Belt and Pennine Escarpment Meltwater Channel System (Cumbria, UK). Morphology, Sedimentology and Formation', *Proceedings of the Geologists Association* **121**, pp423-443.

Livingstone, S J, Evans, D J A, Ó Cofaigh, C, Davies, B J, Merritt, J W, Huddart, D, Mitchell, W A, Roberts, D H and Yorke, L, 2012, 'Glaciodynamics of the central sector of the last British-Irish Ice Sheet in Northern England', *Earth-Science Reviews* **111**, pp25-55.

Lunn, A G 1995a, 'Quaternary', in Johnson, G AL, (ed.), 'Robson's Geology of North East England', *Transactions of the Natural History Society of Northumberland* **56** , pp296-311.

Lunn, A G 1995b, 'The Quaternary of South Tynedale', in Scrutton, C (ed.), *Northumbrian rocks and landscape: a field guide.* Yorkshire Geol. Soc. & Ellenbank Press, Maryport, pp137-145.

Lunn, A G, 2004, *Northumberland.* New Naturalist Series. Harper-Collins, London.

Manley, G, 1955, On the occurrence of ice domes and permanently snow-covered summits. *Journal of Glaciology* **2**, pp453-6.

Manley, G, 1959, The Late-Glacial climate of North-west England. *Geological Journal* **2**, pp188-215.

Manley, G, 1961, Solar variations, climatic change and related geophysical problems. *Nature* **190**, pp967-968.

Mills, A B, 1976, View from the crop: a glimpse of the unusual glacial rafting of coal in Durham. *The Opencast Geologist* **1**, pp16-17.

Mills, D A C and Hull, J H, 1976, Geology of the country around Barnard Castle, *Memoir of the Geological Survey of Great Britain.*

Mitchell, W A (ed.), 1991, *Western Pennines: Field Guide.* Quaternary Research Association, London.

Mitchell, W A, 2007, 'Reconstructions of the Late Devensian (Dimlington Stadial) British-Irish Ice Sheet: the role of the upper Tees drumlin field, northern Pennines, England', *Proceedings of the Yorkshire Geological Society* **56**, pp221–234.

Mitchell, W A and Huddart, D, 2002, Cross Fell (NY 687 344), in: Huddart, D and Glasser, N F (eds), *Quaternary of Northern England. Geological Conservation Review Series* **25**, Joint Nature Conservation Committee, Peterborough, pp334-343.

Moore, E N, 1994, *Glacial Geology and Geomorphology of Weardale*. Unpublished PhD thesis, University of Durham.

Raistrick, A, 1931, The late-glacial and post-glacial Periods in the North Pennines, *Transactions of the Northern Naturalists Union* Part I, pp16-29.

Rowell, A J and Turner, J S, 1952, Corrie-glaciation in the upper Eden Valley, Westmorland. *Geological Journal* **1**, pp200-207.

Syverson, K M, Mickelson, D M, 2009, Origin and significance of lateral meltwater channels formed along a temperate glacier margin, Glacier Bay, Alaska. *Boreas* **38**, pp132–145.

Taylor, B J, Burgess, I C, Land, D H, Mills, D A C, Smith, D B and Warren, M A, 1971, *Northern England*. Fourth edition. British Regional Geology. Natural Environment Research Council, Institute of Geological Sciences, HMSO: London.

Trotter, F M, 1929, 'On the glaciation of eastern Edenside, Alston Block and the Carlisle Plain', *Quarterly Journal of the Geological Society of London* **85**, pp549-612.

Vincent, P J, 1969, *The glacial history and deposits of a selected part of the Alston Block*, PhD thesis, University of Durham.

Wilson, P and Clark, R, 1995, 'Landforms associated with a Loch Lomond Stadial glacier at Cronkley Scar, Teesdale, northern Pennines', *Proceedings of the Yorkshire Geological Society* **50**, pp277-283.

Chapter 5

Flora and vegetation

Margaret E Bradshaw

Introduction

The flora of Upper Teesdale is probably more widely known than that of any other area in Britain, and yet perhaps only a few of the thousands who visit the Dale each year realise the extent to which the vegetation and flora contribute to the essence of its character. In the valley, the meadows in the small walled fields extend, in the lower part, far up the south-facing slope, and, until 1957 to almost 570 m at Grass Hill, then the highest farm in England. On the north face, the ascent of the meadows is abruptly cut off from the higher, browner fells by the Whin Sill cliff, marked by a line of quarries. Below High Force, the floor of the valley has a general wooded appearance which is provided by the small copses and the many isolated trees growing along the

Pennine skyline above
Calcareous grassland and wet
bog, Red Sike Moss
© Margaret E Bradshaw

Spring gentian
© Geoff Herbert

walls and bordering the river. Above High Force is a broader, barer valley which merges with the expansive fells leading up to the characteristic skyline of Great Dun Fell, Little Dun Fell and Cross Fell.

Within this region of fairly typical North Pennine vegetation is a comparatively small area which contains many species of flowering plants, ferns, mosses, liverworts and lichens which can be justifiably described as rare. The best known is, of course, the spring gentian *(Gentiana verna)*, but this is only one of a remarkable collection of plants of outstanding scientific value. For generations of British naturalists, Upper Teesdale has been hallowed ground, and many still come each year to 'pay their respects' to the relics of an earlier, more widespread flora. For those on more serious business, the unique plant communities are of major scientific importance and provide abundant opportunities for ecological and taxonomic research.

The account that follows is divided into two parts. The first deals, broadly, with the valleys and lower lying regions of the Dale (up to about 460 m) and the second with the vegetation of the higher ground. The line between the two is not very sharply drawn; where there is some overlap, cross-references are given.

Normally, when a plant is first mentioned, both its English and Latin names are given, and subsequently its English name only. Bryophytes (liverworts, mosses) and lichens have Latin names only. Plant community types are shown according to the National Vegetation Classification scheme, for example as (NVC MG3). For more details see Averis (2013) and Averis *et al.* (2004).

Flora and vegetation of lower ground

Meadows and pastures

In the last 60 years, there have been great changes in the farming practices in the Dale. These have affected the management of the meadows and pastures, particularly in the valley floor. Tractors and herds of suckler-cows have replaced horses and dairy cows, and the production of cross-bred ewes and lambs and butcher-ready lambs has become common. The application of artificial fertiliser has increased to boost the growth of the grass to be made into silage or haylage, though sheep farmers like to make some 'soft hay' for the sheep. These changes have resulted in fewer herb-rich meadows of the old type, described below, and more uniformly green fields, rich in buttercups and reddish-brown soury-dock and fewer of the other colourful flowering plants eg. wood crane's-bill *(Geranium sylvaticum)*. In the upper part of the Dale the meadows are now being grazed for longer periods in the year and some are becoming pastures, because modern transport allows other fodder — silage, straw and hay — to be brought in. The agricultural support introduced some 20–35 years ago to encourage more environmentally friendly lower stocking and fertiliser application was only partially successful in restoring a more bio-diverse landscape. Let's hope that a new 'farmer selected' system produces better results.

Meadows

The plants of the meadows and the roadside verges attract attention by the rich variety of their colour. In early May the common dandelions burst forth in a blaze of golden yellow, and the creamy-white sweet cicely *(Myhrris odorata)* lines some road and riverbanks. Throughout the summer, except when the meadows are newly cut for hay, a succession of colours attract the eye because of an unusually large proportion of colourful flowering plants amongst the grasses. Such meadows are known locally as 'herbie meadows' and by the botanists as 'herb-rich'. Almost a hundred different kinds of flowering plants have been recorded in them,

Herb-rich meadow,Tattyfield,
Baldersdale 2007
© John O'Reilly

but the composition of individual meadows varies considerably with such factors as altitude, aspect, soil, drainage and farming methods. Whilst grasses form the basis, wood crane's-bill, now much scarcer, earthnut *(Conopodium majus),* meadow buttercup *(Ranunculus acris)* and sorrel *(Rumex acetosa),* locally known as 'soury dock', are mainly responsible for their pink-purple, white, yellow and reddish appearance in the summer. At least eight kinds of grasses are usually present, and of these the most constant are sweet vernal *(Anthoxanthum odoratum),* sheep's fescue *(Festuca ovina),* crested dog's-tail *(Cynosurus cristatus)* and cock's-foot

(Dactylis glomerata). Many other flowering plants are present, such as red and white clover *(Trifolium pratense and T. repens)*, ribwort plantain *(Plantago lanceolata)*, dandelion *(Taraxacum* agg.*)* and later in the year another dandelion-like plant, rough hawkbit *(Leontodon hispidus)*. One group of plants of particular interest to the more knowledgeable is Lady's mantle *(Alchemilla vulgaris* agg*)*. This will be familiar enough with its attractive fan-like leaves and masses of small yellow-green flowers. In Teesdale there are nine species, of which three are almost confined to Teesdale and three more are only thinly scattered in the North Pennines and three are frequent. Here and there are patches of bistort *(Polygonum bistorta)*. Meadows such as these were usually found on the better-drained slopes where the soil is a fine, crumbly loam, often enriched by the lime-rich water which seeps from the bands of limestone rocks in the hillsides. Today, such floriferous meadows are much less frequent, but in recent years the less-rich have been enhanced by the spreading of 'green hay' from neighbouring richer fields, in the hope that seed will germinate and become established plants.

In the wetter parts, the more marsh-like vegetation contains other interesting species. Most striking is the majestic melancholy thistle *(Cirsium heterophyllum)*, known locally as 'shaving brushes', with its tall, stiff stems and solitary purple heads. Here, too, are water avens *(Geum rivale)*, ragged robin *(Silene floscuculi)*, marsh valerian *(Valeriana dioica)*, meadow sweet *(Filipendula ulmaria)* and marsh hawk's-beard *(Crepis paludosa)* which is another plant with flowers like a small dandelion. Somewhat hidden amongst this tall vegetation are the marsh orchids, which hold a fascination for almost every plant hunter.

Cronkley meadow in the 1960s before it was 'improved'
© Margaret E Bradshaw

Records made in 1967 of the occurrences of globeflower *(Trollius europaeus)*, wood crane's-bill and melancholy thistle in Forest-in-Teesdale, around Newbiggin and Holwick, and Mickleton showed different distribution patterns for each species in each area. In a 2000 repeat survey (Bradshaw, 2001) the declines were greater in the Newbiggin/Holwick than in Forest-in-Teesdale meadows.

The meadows of the higher Dalc show certain differences. In spring, some of these are dominated by shades of yellow: first marsh marigold, then buttercups and the paler globeflower (NVC MG8). Globeflowers are more frequent here but much rarer than in former times; they have the delightfully apt local name of 'double dumplings'. Wood anemones *(Anemone nemorosa)* grow in the open fields and it is not surprising that a local child wondered why they were called wood anemones. Another not uncommon woodland plant is goldilocks *(Ranunculus auricomus)*, though nowhere do bluebells grow

Crested Dog's-tail — Marsh Marigold community (NVC MG8) and inset marsh marigold
© Dave Mitchell

Ash — Rowan — Dog's Mercury woodland. Inset top left Wood Sorrell, bottom left dog's mercury and right wood false-broome.
© Dave Mitchell

in the open as they do in Swaledale. These three are all 'woodland plants'. Here also is the mountain pansy *(Viola lutea)* — purple, purple and white, purple and yellow, but rarely the wholly yellow flower so common in Swaledale and Craven. Wood crane's-bill does not seem to like the exposed conditions and is only found occasionally in sheltered places such as amongst the willows near Cronkley Farm, although its leaves can be found in the turf on Widdybank Fell at 525 m. In the higher Dale some of the fields, especially those near the becks and with limestone outcrops, contain more uncommon species such as alpine bistort *(Polygonum vivipara)*, northern bedstraw *(Galium boreale)*, shady horsetail *(Equisetum pratense)*, mountain eyebright *(Euphrasia officinalis* ssp. *monticola)* and two small and peculiar ferns, moonwort *(Botrychium lunaria)* and adder's tongue *(Ophioglossum vulgartum)*.

In a few places there still persist two ancient introductions. One is northern dock *(Rumex longifolius)*, the other is masterwort *(Imperatoria ostruthium)* — a herb which was used as a cow medicine in the upper Dale — whilst lower down, green hellebore *(Helleborus viridis)* was used for the same purpose and still survives near Cotherstone below Middleton. It is also possible that the three lady's mantles peculiar to the Teesdale area were introduced as medicinal herbs from Central Europe or Scandinavia.

It is almost certain that the meadows in Teesdale have been directly derived from the former more extensive woodlands. Several of the meadow plants — wood anemone, goldilocks and wood crane's-bill — are essentially woodland species (NVC W9,W16). A fine example of a transition from herb-rich, birch-willow woodland to meadow can be seen near Force Garth. There is great similarity between these hay-meadows and the park-meadows in mid-Sweden. Although the Swedish meadows contain many more species, almost all of the Teesdale plants are there. In Sweden the meadows are found in clearings in the herb-rich, open birch and spruce woodlands, and the high fertility of the soil is maintained by natural flushing of the soils with mineral-rich spring water and shed leaves of the birch.

Pastures

In the Forest-in-Teesdale and lower Harwood area, the floor of the valley is covered by a series of drumlins — low lying hillocks of glacial till (boulder clay) — and rocks left by the melting glaciers. This landscape can be seen clearly from the road from Cow Green to Langdon Beck and its composition at places where the Tees has eroded the drumlins near Widdybank Farm and near Cronkley Bridge. Here, meadows give way to a larger number of permanent pastures and the vegetation loses its more obvious summer-time brilliance; but some of these fields are far from being botanically dull.

Where the Whin Sill is near the surface, the pastures are poor and are covered by an acid turf of mat-grass *(Nardus stricta)* with tormentil *(Potentilla erecta)* and heath bedstraw *(Galium saxatile)* (NVC U5). Locally there are patches of deergrass *(Trichophorum germanicum)*, bilberry *(Vaccinium myrtillus)* and species of bog-moss *(Sphagnum* spp.*)*. This plant community is better represented in the upland region and is described below.

That a few of the hollows are water-logged is indicated by the dominance of the vegetation by rushes, mainly the soft rush *(Juncus effusus)* and sharp flowered rush *(J. acutiflorus)* (NVC MG8). Growing with these are such plants as ragged robin and sneezewort *(Achillea ptarmica)*, a relative of the common yarrow, which was formerly dried, ground and used as snuff.

Further west and on the lower slopes of Widdybank Fell, plant hunters quicken their pace making for the broken turfy pastures, a problem to the farmer but a botanist's delight. These 'turfy marshes' (NVC M10, M11) have been described in some detail by Pigott (1956). They have developed where the springs or seepage water ooze out of the drumlins and till-covered hillsides. Their general appearance ranges from a slightly broken, 'boggy' pasture to a patchwork of hummocks, more or less isolated from one another by an expanse of calcareous, muddy gravel. They carry some of the richest plant communities in Teesdale. At the right time of the year they are covered with a haze of pink caused by the masses of bird's-eye primroses *(Primula farinosa)*; and in a few places one could have been forgiven for thinking that alpine bartsia *(Bartsia alpina)* is a common plant, but not so now. Other showy species include spring gentian, northern marsh orchid *(Dactylorhiza purpurella)*, early marsh orchid *(D. incarnata)* and grass of Parnassus *(Parnassia palustris)*. Among the less obvious plants of great scientific importance that grow here are two sedges: hair sedge *(Carex capillaris)* and false sedge *(Kobresia simpliciuscula)*, the rushes, northern deergrass *(Trichophorum cespitosum)*, variegated horsetail *(Equisetum variegatum)* and sea plantain *(Plantago maritima)*.

The open, broken nature of these habitats is largely due to trampling by grazing animals; in former times by red deer and even aurochs, and more recently by domesticated animals, especially cattle. In the extreme cases, active springs wash away much of the exposed silt and clay, leaving hummocks of vegetation on an almost bare gentle slope of calcareous mud. These hummocks support an intriguing mixture of very common and rare plants; for example, alpine bartsia and false sedge share the tops with daisy *(Bellis perennis)* and dandelion; and butterwort *(Pinguicula vulgaris)*, grass of Parnassus and yellow mountain saxifrage *(Saxifraga aizoides)* grow on the sides. There are few grasses on these hummocks but they do include the strange combination of blue moor-grass *(Sesleria caerulea)*, usually a plant of dry places, and purple moor-grass *(Molinia caerulea)*, usually a plant of wet places. Many sedges and some rushes are present as well as a rich bryophyte flora. Between the hummocks, the few species include marsh marigold, lesser spearwort *(Ranunculus flammula)* and marsh arrowgrass *(Triglochin palustris)*. Earlier this century the introduced heavier cattle churned up the soft substrate, impeding the free movement of the water and hoof-holes created small stagnant pools. Ten years later the swift flow of the water along the man-created channel has recreated the silty base and many of the original plants are there; but the hoof-holed substrate of the low-sedge-marsh vegetation through which the water used to seep has not recovered. This century the gradual spread of rushes has entered most of these communities.

In the adjacent meadows where cattle-trampling is less frequent, there is an almost closed turf with much purple moor-grass, clumps of globeflower and wood crane's-bill. Although bird's-eye primrose, spring gentian and even alpine bartsia may occur here, most of the other smaller rare species are absent.

By the riverside, a rather similar unstable open community is maintained by natural forces (NVC M10,M11). Here, at Cetry Bank, on the outside of a curve, the Tees cuts into the base of a moraine. Seepage and springs keep the calcareous till permanently wet and after rain, or when the snow thaws, the whole mass becomes semi-fluid. Under these conditions tussocks of turf dominated by purple moor-grass and blue moor-grass build up, and become the home of the less vigorous species such as alpine bartsia, spring gentian, bird's-eye primrose, wild thyme, Scottish asphodel *(Tofieldia pusilla)*, hair sedge, alpine rush *(Juncus alpinoarticulatus)* and lesser clubmoss *(Selaginella selaginoides)*. Here too are cushions of two mosses, *Tortella tortuosa* and *Ctenidium molluscum*. Nothing is stable for long, and eventually the ridge of plants becomes too large and either slides down the slope or rolls over. The pockets of wet mud and gravel are occupied by such plants as yellow mountain saxifrage, yellow sedge *(Carex lepidocarpa)*, false sedge and the moss *Scorpidium revolvens*.

On this unstable bank the continued existence of this species-rich flora would appear to depend upon a balance between the slow build-up of vegetation and its breakdown due to erosion of the bank. The periodic removal of the accumulated boulders and clayey mess from the base, when the river is in spate, may be a vital factor. A little further down the river, but separated from it by an alluvial flat, is another moraine slope covered with stable, bent-fescue turf, a little heather and a few springs and flushes, indicator of a former course of the Tees. In contrast is Hag Hill, a steep-faced moraine where the Tees actively scours the base at all times; much of the vegetation has gone completely because the rapid and continuous erosion has created an over-steepened and hence unstable slope. Since the completion of the Cow Green dam in 1971 and the regulation of water flow in the Tees, the slope has become more vegetated. Some open habitats remain with such rare plants as field gentian *(Gentianella campestris)*. Thus, a limited amount of erosion by the river seems to be desirable, but to maintain the rare flora the undisturbed periods when the river is low may also be of importance.

In other parts of the Dale there are more till hillocks, where the internal water table is high and seepage occurs out of the sides. Here, a less extreme form of soil creep takes place. Miniature terraces develop and provide sufficient instability to form a habitat for some of the smaller plants, such as spring gentian, lesser clubmoss and moonwort amongst fescue and bent.

Where the smaller tributaries of the Tees (the sikes) meander through the flatter ground, alluvial flats have arisen. These are frequently flushed with silt and calcareous material which maintains a high base-status. Here is a flora very similar to that of the 'turfy marshes' but perhaps especially noteworthy for the high density of bird's-eye primroses.

Woodlands

The fragments of more or less natural (not planted) woodland which survive scarcely provide a representative picture of this once widespread vegetation. Sizeable relics occur only by the river above and below High Force and at Park End near Holwick; elsewhere the woods consist of rather scrubby patches on the cliff faces and by the streams.

Most of the woodland on the better drained soils has been replaced by meadows, but a little does remain, such as Sun Wood above High Force (NVC W9). Here are birch *(Betula pubescens)*, ash *(Fraxinus excelsior)*, hazel *(Corylus avellana)*, bird-cherry *(Prunus padus)*, rowan *(Sorbus aucuparia)* and the common sallow *(Salix cinerea* ssp. *oleifolia)*. The ground flora contains many typical woodland plants, such as wood anemone, common violet *(Viola riviniana)*, wood-sorrel *(Oxalis acetosella)* and bitter vetch *(Lathyrus linifolius)*; globeflower, earth nut, wood crane's-bill, and lady's mantle are also found. Woods of this kind must have been the first to be cleared, for the rich brown earth soil is similar to that in the meadows. In the wetter places by streams and springs, and a few water-logged hollows, alder *(Alnus glutinosa)* and several willows are frequent. Though the common sallow is the most frequent, four other willows are often found; eared willow *(S. aurita)*, dark leaved willow *(S. myrsinifolia)* — now very rare, tea-leaved willow *(S. phylicifolia)*, and creeping willow *(S. repens)* which flowers and seeds happily under the annual mowing in at least one meadow. In these places the herbs are those of a fen or marsh as, for example, marsh marigold, marsh thistle *(Cirsium palustre)*, marsh hawk's-beard, meadowsweet, water avens, ragged robin, globeflower, heath spotted orchid *(Dactylorhiza maculata* ssp. *ericetorum)* and several rushes. The similarity between these communities and the wetter meadows is readily seen; near Cronkley Farm the much-nibbled remains of willow bushes illustrate the process by which this valley has come to be virtually treeless.

Juniper, 2011
© Dave Mitchell

A somewhat different birch woodland (NVC W11) occurs at Park End. Here the birches are 10 m to 12 m high and at least 30 cm in diameter, indicating considerable age; like most of the other woods it is open to grazing and so doomed to extinction unless regeneration can be encouraged. This wood is on Whin Sill, where the soil is more acidic, and bluebells and bracken are common. Both are characteristic of oak woodlands in other parts of the Pennines. It is of considerable interest to note that some of the birches are of a northern race *(Betula pubescens* ssp. *tortuosa),* which can be recognised by the pungent resinous smell of its small leaves after wetting by rain.

On the south side of the river, in the National Nature Reserve, the north-facing hillside is covered with another kind of relict woodland (NVC W19). This is dominated by juniper *(Juniperus communis),* a low-growing evergreen native conifer which grows in a fantastic mixture of columnar and bushy shapes, and locally forms impenetrable thickets. The juniper occurs over an extensive area by both sides of the Tees from Keedholm Scar to the summit of Cronkley Fell; in a few places where grazing is limited some regeneration is taking place, but for the most part only the resistant old trees survive. Formerly this 'jinifer' was gathered for firewood. In 2012 a deadly, water-borne pathogen was found to be killing the bushes. These are being cut down and burnt *in situ* but alas, five years later the pathogen continues to spread.

Here and near Holwick Head Bridge a dozen or so different kinds of fern can be found; amongst these are lemon-scented fern *(Oreopteris limbosperma)* which is covered with small yellow glandular hairs and smells of lemons, the handsome male fern *(Dryopteris borreri)* and two smaller and more delicate ferns with tree names, oak fern *(Gymnocarpium dryopteris)* and beech fern *(Phegopteris connectilis)*.

Juniper woodland in Teesdale is extensive, and isolated bushes, often of low growth, are scattered far over the slopes of Mickle Fell. Isolated trees of birch and aspen on Cronkley Scar and Falcon Clints, together with the more widespread willow scrub which extends into Harwood Dale, all indicate that this now bare part of the Dale must have enjoyed the shelter of at least a sparse covering of trees and bushes within historic times. Protected from grazing, the mutilated remnants would recover to provide windbreaks and reduce the present bleakness.

Riversides

The riverside communities are amongst the most interesting in the Dale. Unlike the meadows and woodlands, the plant communities have bare or 'open' areas. The most important process in the maintenance of this open condition is a large fluctuation in the flow of the river. Even after the construction of Cow Green reservoir very high spates do occur when the reservoir is overflowing and/or Maize Beck is in flood. The Tees has many tributaries and there is evidence that it has changed its course in many places, so open vegetation by the river will have always existed and been available to support the many rare species including: very rare hawkweeds, shrubby cinquefoil *(Potentilla fruticosa)*, globeflowers, shady and variegated horsetails, flat sedge *(Blysmus compressus)*, alpine (viviparous) bistort, northern bedstraw and more.

The margins of the wide stony bed of the Tees provide a habitat for those species which can withstand the force of the river in spate, after heavy rain or when the winter snow melts. That some of the rarer plants of the area can do so no doubt explains, at least in part, their survival to this day. Most characteristic of this habitat is shrubby cinquefoil, a small bush which becomes covered with a fine display of yellow, rose-like flowers for many weeks in the summer. This plant grows in dense stands in several places or is scattered singly by the river from Falcon Clints to below Middleton. Its deep roots and tough stems enable it to survive the pressure of the flood water even when almost completely submerged and it is of interest to know that it occupies very similar riverside habitats in the Ural mountains in Russia. Formerly a large colony existed at the margin of a former course of the Tees several hundred metres from the present course of the Tees and separated from it by heather heath.

Plants in the fine gravel and silt amongst the stones include sea plantain and scurvy-grass *(Cochlearia pyrenaica)*, two maritime plants not uncommon in some inland mountain areas, as well as northern bedstraw, bird's-eye primrose, blue moor-grass, alpine bistort, stone bramble *(Rubus saxatilis)*; grass of Parnassus and salad burnet *(Poterium sanguisorba* ssp. *sanguisorba)*. On the more stable banks, where the soil is deeper, the flora is essentially that of the herb-rich woodland and hay meadows already described (NVC MG3,W9,W11). These are at their best where the riverside path has been fenced off from the adjacent fields thus excluding grazing animals but not rabbits. The broken border of trees, mainly willow, alder, bird-cherry and ash, give some protection to the herbs from river erosion but not, alas, from trampling and picking. Additional species not commonly found in the meadows include the meadow, the wood and the variegated horsetail, early purple and fragrant orchid *(Gymnadenia conopsea)*, twayblade *(Neottia ovata)*, giant bellflower *(Campanula latifolia)*, and three of the rarer Lady's mantles *(Alchemilla monticola, A. wichurae and A. glomerulans)*. Also present is saw-wort *(Serratula tinctoria)*, a species at the northern end of its range.

Where the Whin Sill rocks form islands in the river, as at Wynch Bridge, a number of base-loving plants have a precarious hold in the joints of the rock. These include cat's foot *(Antennaria dioica)*, alpine cinquefoil *(Potentilla crantzii)*, alpine penny-cress *(Noccaea caerulescens)* and dwarf golden-rod *(Solidago virgaurea* ssp. *minuta)*. In this region also is rock whitebeam *(Sorbus rupicola)*, a relation of the rowan with simple white-backed leaves and large fruits.

In the gorge below High Force, the waterfall maintains, for most of the time, a humid atmosphere. Here is a rich bryophyte flora, especially on the shaded north-facing slope. Above the waterfall, on the south-facing rock, a lush growth of the woodland herb community contains wood crane's-bill, meadow-sweet, water avens, greater wood-rush *(Luzula sylvatica)* and two sedges: pale sedge *(Carex pallescens)* and wood-sedge *(C. sylvatica)*.

Since the erection of the fence by the Pennine Way that excluded grazing from the Tees bank, and the reduction in the high spates of the Tees, many open sites have become closed, the meadow-type vegetation ranker, the scrub denser and bracken more frequent.

Though in this part of the National Nature Reserve, between Wynch Bridge and Holwick Head Bridge, conservation work is attempting to maintain the three communities of meadow, scrub and woodland.

Whin Sill Scars

The Whin Sill cliffs of Falcon Clints and Cronkley Scar are prominent features of the Forest-in-Teesdale area; less well known are Dine Holm Scar and Holwick Scars.

The well-jointed facies, block scree and rock slopes are well drained and though little peat develops on the more stable slopes, lime-loving plants tend to be absent. The vegetation resembles that of the 'bilberry edges' of the South Pennines. The most abundant species are heather, bilberry, cowberry *(Vaccinium vitis-idaea)*, crowberry *(Empetrum nigrum)* and wavy hair-grass *(Deschampsia flexuosa)*, but locally bearberry *(Arctostaphylos uva-ursi)* is co-dominant with these species, (possibly a remnant of NVC H13). On the drier sunnier aspects, bell heather *(Erica cinerea)* is common, and it is on these screes that the locally rare parsley fern *(Cryptogramma crispa)* can be found. Formerly, the little arctic-alpine fern oblong woodsia *(Woodsia ilvensis)* grew on the Whin Sill cliffs near Cauldron Snout, but it appears to have suffered from the avidity of collectors (plants grown from a mixture of spores from Wales and Scotland have been introduced at sites on both sides of the Tees). Green and maidenhair spleenworts *(Asplenium viride* and *A. trichomanes)* and holly fern *(Polystichum lonchitis)* still occur sparingly on Falcon Clints. The moss flora contains several woodland species; and locally, in damp hollows, patches of bryophytes (including bog moss) and lichens characteristic of acid rocks are present. Indications of an earlier woody vegetation on these scars are provided by the isolated plants of birch, aspen, rowan and juniper; and by the occurrence on south-facing ledges of a tall-herb community with greater wood-rush, stinging nettle *(Urtica dioica)*, dog's mercury *(Mercurialis perennis)*, red campion *(Silene dioica)*, rosebay willow-herb *(Chamerion angustifolium)* and orpine *(Sedum telephium)*.

The Whin Sill cliffs at High Cup Nick are outside our area, but it is worth noting that they have a number of mountain plants not found in Teesdale, such as the roseroot *(Sedum rosea)* and Alpine saxifrage *(Saxifraga nivalis)*.

Flora and vegetation of higher ground

The more upland areas of Upper Teesdale are characterised by four principal types of vegetation: blanket bog, dwarf shrub heath, grass heath and flush vegetation.

Blanket Bog

Much of upland Teesdale up to 600 m lies buried beneath a blanket of acid peat, varying in thickness from 30 cm to 4 m; the peat is characteristic of the flatter and gently sloping areas. Most of it is of a type which depends for its formation on acid conditions, an adequate supply of rain and a topography which tends to retard water run-off. Under these conditions, the bog moss *(Sphagnum)*, which is the chief peat former, becomes established; and once established, it continues to grow. As the older parts below die, they fail to decay due to the water-logging of the acid environment; and ultimately the dead bog moss becomes compressed to form peat. Pollen analysis has revealed that peat development in Teesdale, as elsewhere in the uplands of England and Scotland, commenced towards the end of the Boreal

Heather — Hare's-tail cotton grass community (Blanket mire) (NVC M19). Inset left to right, hare's-tail cotton grass, *Hylocomium splendens, Rhytidiadelphus loreus* and cloudberry.
© Dave Mitchell

Period, and spread rapidly between about 7,000 and 5,000 years ago during the wetter Atlantic period. At the base of this peat, remains of trees, mainly pine, birch, willow and juniper, can be seen in many places where exposed by erosion and stand witness to the former extent of woodland. Remains of the common reed *(Phragmites australis),* of species of *Equisetum* and of the now rare British moss *Paludella squarrosa* are also locally abundant in the lower peat and it seems that they must have been constituents of the ground vegetation in wet, shaded parts of the original woodland.

The present-day vegetation of these bogs depends largely on the extent to which they have been burned, drained or grazed. Where relatively undisturbed (NVC M17, N18), a good cover of bog moss is still to be found supporting on its surface such plants as the sundew *(Drosera rotundifolia)* and the bog asphodel *(Narthecium ossifragum).* Growing through the carpet are heather, cross-leaved heath *(Erica tetralix),* tussocks of the tufted hare's-tail cotton-grass *(Eriophorum vaginatum),* shoots of the common cotton-grass *(E. angustifolium)* and deergrass. Decaying animal matter on the wet bog surface provides the habitat for the mosses *Splachnum sphaericum* and *Tetraplodon mnioides* and for the very rare moss *Aplodon wormskioldii*, known elsewhere only on Ben Lawers in Scotland. A patch of this moss, almost 2 m in length, was observed growing on what must have been the carcass of a sheep submerged in a peat pool. The rediscovery in 1965, on the blanket bog on Widdybank Fell, of the dwarf birch *(Betula nana)* provided not only an important addition to the arctic-alpine element of the Upper Teesdale flora but also the first recent living record in England. On bogs which have been subjected to man's interference (NVC M19), the bog moss with its associated species is poorly represented and the heather and hare's-tail cotton-grass tend to become dominant; in drained bogs, cloudberry *(Rubus chamaemorus)*, cowberry and fir clubmoss *(Huperzia selago)* may be present.

In many parts of upland Teesdale, rapid erosion of peat has resulted in exposure of the mineral soil below. Wind, water and frost are the chief agents of erosion but the initiating causes are not yet fully understood. In recent decades revegetation has taken place naturally and has also aided by the blocking of the drainage 'grips' created after World War Two.

Dwarf Shrub Heath

The principal dwarf shrub heath community of the Teesdale area is that dominated by heather *(Calluna vulgaris)*, and its presence indicates an oceanic tendency in the otherwise sub-arctic climate of the region. The community is found wherever better drained, leached and acid soils occur. Thus, the heather moor (heath) (NVC H9, H12) is characteristic of the steeper slopes and the well-drained flatter areas; impeded drainage results in

Heather, bilberry
© Dave Mitchell

the development of blanket bog. The heath soils are overlaid by a shallow layer of acid humus — peat. It is now generally agreed that heather moor communities lying within the potential forest zone are largely man-made, resulting initially from the early clearance of the open forest and subsequently maintained as heath in the last two centuries by the practice of moor-burning and grazing. In Teesdale, as elsewhere, heather provides valuable grazing for grouse and sheep, and the periodic burning of the heather is to ensure a succession of young heather shoots. The maintenance of heather moorland is thus of considerable economic importance for the farmers and sporting interests in the area.

The floristic composition of heather moor varies considerably depending mainly on the intensity of burning and grazing. Frequent burning produces dense even-aged stands of heather with little else present except an under-storey of bryophytes and lichens. Where the community is more open, common constituents are bilberry, cowberry, bell-heather, crowberry, tormentil, heath bedstraw, wavy hair-grass and sheep's fescue; in wetter areas cross-leaved heath is also often present (NVC H10). In undisturbed areas, lesser twayblade *(Neottia cordata)* can still be found, often growing in a patch of moss. It seems likely that the juniper was formerly a constituent of some of the heather communities on the less acid soils but today only scattered bushes remain. Heather with good juniper does still occur on the Whin Sill outcrop near High Force.

Grass Heath

The grass heath communities of the higher ground and fell tops are also a product of man's activities. Some of this grassland on the better soils — the fescue-bent-thyme and fescue-bent-heath bedstraw grasslands (NVC CG10, U4) — has been produced directly from former forest or scrub as a consequence of long-sustained grazing, latterly mainly by sheep. This prevented, in the first place, regeneration of the woodland by the eating of the seedling trees and secondly, favoured the grasses of the field layer at the expense of the other herbs. In grasses, the growing point is at the base of the shoot and is not damaged by grazing unless very intensive; in contrast, in many herbs, though not all, the growing point lies well above ground level and is, therefore, much more liable to damage. In this way, grassland directly replaced forest in the uplands. On the other hand, some of the grass heath is secondary in origin, having been derived again as a result of grazing but this time from heather moor which, in its turn, was produced from forest. Ratcliffe (1959, 1962), has shown that for North Wales, the Southern Uplands and the Highlands of Scotland, the sub-montane heather communities have been, and are still being, replaced by bilberry communities, bent-fescue grassland and mat-grass communities as a result of repeated heather burning combined with intensive sheep grazing; and this is probably happening in Teesdale too. These man-made communities, like the heather moor, are again of economic importance to the farmers and sporting interests of the Dale.

At the highest levels on Mickle Fell and Crossfell, some grass heath unmodified by man may exist (NVC U10). This view is strengthened by the occurrence in these poor grasslands of species like the stiff sedge *(Carex bigelowii)* and the alpine clubmoss *(Diphasiastrum alpinum)* and by the presence of several characteristic lichens and mosses for example *Polytrichastrum alpinum* (NVC U7).

Although no detailed ecological investigation of the Teesdale grass heath as a whole has been carried out, it can be shown, following the work of McVean and Ratcliffe (1962) for the Highlands of Scotland, that types of grass heath represented in Upper Teesdale depend, in addition to the grazing factor, on the soil-moisture regime and the base-status of the soil. In soils of high base-status, lime is present together with salts of magnesium, potassium, ammonium and sodium and such soils are usually fertile; in soils of low base-status, free lime is usually absent and the other bases are present only in small quantities; these soils are usually infertile.

In Upper Teesdale there are three main kinds of grassland on soils of low base-status; they are dominated by bent and fescue, mat-grass and purple moor-grass respectively and they are all species-poor. There are also limestone grasslands, dominated by a variety of grasses and herbs, which are species-rich. The grasslands will be described briefly in this order.

Bent-Fescue grassland (species-poor)

This grassland (NVC U4), in which the bent grasses, *(Agrostis capillaris* and *A. vinealis)* and the sheep's fescue are the dominants, is characteristic of the less acid and more fertile soils, provided that drainage is reasonably free. Other characteristic plants of the community are sweet vernal-grass, tormentil, heath bedstraw, common dog-violet, field wood-rush and the mosses *Rhytidiadelphus squarrosus* and *Hylocomium splendens*. The lovely mountain pansy is also often present. This type of grassland, together with the limestone pastures, provides the mainstay of the grazing animal in Upper Teesdale.

Mat-grass grassland

Floristically this is very similar to bent-fescue grassland

except that the mat-grass replaces the other two grasses as dominant (NVC U5). The soils are acid and tend to be wetter, particularly during the winter months. The wetter conditions result in the dominance of mat-grass, especially where grazing pressure is high; it is more unpalatable to sheep than the other grasses though in the early summer its young leaves are eaten. The moss layer tends to be better developed and the heath rush *(Juncus squarrosus)*, the pill sedge *(Carex pilulifera)* and the wavy hair-grass are other characteristic species (NVC U6). The presence of dwarf heather and bilberry, and more rarely the wood anemone, indicates not only the possible origin of this grassland type but also what it would develop into if the grazing pressure were reduced.

Purple moor grass (Molinia) grassland

Purple moor grass prefers still wetter soils, but not usually waterlogged. Consequently it is characteristic of the heavier soils with impeded drainage and of soils where lateral movement of water takes place as in flush sites (NVC M25). In these soils anaerobic conditions prevail and iron salts occur in the ferrous condition, imparting a blue-grey colour to the soil. Such soils are described as 'gleyed' and are often overlaid by an accumulation of amorphous peat. In addition to the purple moor grass, most of the other grasses already mentioned (except the wavy hair-grass) and heath rush are present in varying quantities. The wetter conditions also favour the presence of a number of sedges, such as carnation sedge *(Carex panicea)*, glaucous sedge *(C. flacca)*, star sedge *(C. echinata)*, pill sedge, dioecious sedge *(C. dioica)* and common sedge *(C. nigra)*. The number of other flowering plants present depends on the base-status of the soil, and from the more fertile soils the list can be extensive. Pure stands of purple moor grass are uncommon in Teesdale and the one near Cronkley Farm has been drained.

In the flushed sites where spring or other water (frequently calcareous) flows laterally through the soil, jointed rush *(Juncus articulatus)* often becomes co-dominant with the purple moor grass. The calcareous flushes provide some of the most species-rich habitats in Upper Teesdale. The description above of the 'turfy marshes' applies equally to these higher flushes, and need not be repeated here.

Grasslands on limestone (species-rich)

This type of grassland is best described under the two headings of sugar-limestone grassland and unaltered limestone grassland.

Sugar Limestone Grassland Blue moor-grass – mountain bedstraw grassland

Sugar limestone exposure, calcareous grassland
© Margaret E Bradshaw

This remarkable grassland type (NVC CG9), has been studied by Professor Pigott and the late Mr Kenneth Park; the following account draws largely on the published work (Pigott, 1956). Like the vegetation it supports, sugar limestone is a unique type of rock, possessing a coarsely crystalline structure. Good outcrops are to be found on the top of Cronkley Fell and again on the west-south-west slope of Widdybank Fell; these outcrops overlie the Whin Sill. On weathering, this metamorphic limestone breaks down to form separate crystals, producing a white limestone sand which closely resembles coarse granulated sugar. The highly calcareous soils which are produced are usually shallow, averaging some 20 cm in depth, but differ from normal limestone soils in the very

high proportion of calcite crystals present and in the virtual absence of siliceous material. Where close turf has developed on top, in the more sheltered areas, black soot-like humus is incorporated in the soil, giving it a brown or blackish colour, and the whole profile is saturated with bases. Below this soil, the underlying sugar limestone is often weathered and stained pale yellow and this zone can be penetrated by roots. This is probably particularly important in relation to the survival of shrubby plants, such as the rock-roses, mountain avens and thyme, which form important constituents of the turf. The presence of buried turf horizons in these soils indicates successive and often progressive burial by fresh wind-blown deposits of limestone sand derived from erosion areas nearby, and this will be mentioned again below.

As already mentioned, these soils occur only in the more sheltered regions and characteristically support a smooth closed turf in which several of the rare species show their greatest vigour. Floristically, the turf is very rich, with as many as 40 to 50 species in a four square

Teesdale (rock) violet
© Margaret E Bradshaw

metre quadrat. Sheep's fescue is dominant with an abundance of the two lime-loving grasses, blue moor-grass *(Sesleria caerulea)* and crested hair-grass *(Koeleria macrantha)*; meadow oat grass *(Avenula pratensis)* and very dwarfed quaking-grass *(Briza media)* are also usually present (NVC CG9). Other characteristic flowering plants present in some quantity are the sedges: spring sedge *(Carex caryophyllea)*, rare spring sedge *(Carex ericetorum)*, hair sedge, limestone bedstraw *(Galium sterneri)*, felwort *(Gentianella amarella)*, common rock-rose *(Helianthemum nummularium)*, purging flax *(Linum catharticum)*, spring sandwort *(Minuartia verna)*, common dog-violet, wild thyme *(Thymus polytrichus)*, harebell *(Campanula rotundifolia)*, ribwort plantain and sea plantain. This century glaucous sedge has become more abundant. Of species generally regarded as rare or local in the British Isles, hoary rock-rose *(Helianthemum oelandicum* ssp. *levigatum)* occurs only on Cronkley Fell and the rock violet *(Viola rupestris)* only on Widdybank Fell. Holly fern is also known from one or two localities.

Three factors contribute to the richness of the vegetation, *viz*: the chemical nature of the soil, the slow accretion of limestone sand from adjacent erosion-areas, and the relatively high grazing intensity (by sheep and rabbits), which reduces the competitive power of the grasses to the advantage of shrubby, rhizomatous and rosette plants. These conditions also prove beneficial to many bryophytes such as *Ditrichum flexicuale, Encalypta streptocarpa, Rhytidium rugosum* (only on Widdybank Fell in Teesdale), *Syntrichia ruralis* ssp. *ruralis, Racomitrium canaescens, Scapania aspera* and also to many lichens. Any attempt at conservation of the sugar limestone grassland must take into account the grazing factor because most of these rarities are termed 'light-demanders' and cannot tolerate being shaded by neighbours as in under-grazed situations

Somewhat surprisingly there is an extensive area overlaying the sugar-limestone on Widdybank Fell which is dominated by short heather, in which such calcicole species as blue moor-grass, spring gentian, alpine bistort and northern bedstraw are frequent and, locally, crowberry is also present. Here the mole-hills are composed of soil which is rich with fragments of sugar limestone rock. Analysis of this soil reveals, among other things, higher clay and quartz sand fractions as compared to normal sugar limestone soil; an explanation of this difference is that the soil in question has been derived from thin glacial drift deposited on top of the sugar limestone outcrop. In contrast to the usual immature sugar limestone soil, these drift-derived soils tend to remain moister during the summer. Where the depth of the overlying drift is greatest, taller heather becomes dominant, forming dry heath communities as already described.

Mention has already been made of the fact that these sugar limestone soils are very liable to erosion when exposed to wind and particularly so when the soil is disturbed by the rubbing of sheep or the scuffling of rabbits. Mole activity too, on the deeper soils, may have contributed to the initial weakening of the turf leading to subsequent erosion. Pigott (1956) describes various stages of erosion leading to the ultimate exposure of bare sugar limestone rock. An initial stage consists of only partial disruption of the turf producing a mosaic of small bare hollows and grass tussocks. Annual species occur in the hollows which soon however become recolonised by seedlings of the spring sandwort, by runners of the wild thyme and by seedlings and persistent fragments of sheep's fescue. More rapid erosion on exposed west-facing slopes results in the progressive undercutting of the turf along numerous edges, bringing about the death of the grasses. Deeper rooted woody plants like the rock-roses and thyme become isolated and may survive for a number of years but ultimately they too are killed. The patch of mountain avens *(Dryas octopetala)*, in the same habitat suffered severely. Large areas of the weathered limestone are laid bare by erosion and are only very slowly re-colonised by plants like fescue and sandwort. A very characteristic plant of these exposed surfaces is the moss *Tortella toruosa*. Eventually, a patchy turf develops and the slow process of soil building starts again. Pigott has aptly described this sugar limestone habitat as not unlike calcareous dunes in miniature. Although, from what has been said, it is obvious that some degree of erosion is beneficial for many of the rare plants, the evidence points to more rapid erosion in recent years and further research is required to devise methods to control this. In the meantime, large areas of the sugar limestone on Cronkley Fell have been fenced to exclude grazing animals, but this can create the new problem of too little grazing. Getting the balance right is being worked out; the amount of grazing by the sheep can be controlled but keeping out the rabbits requires constant effort.

Another consequence of erosion is the development below the outcrops of deeper, moister, dark-brown soils which consist largely of an admixture of blown limestone particles and peat. Alpine meadow rue and false-sedge occur very abundantly in these soils amongst more frequent species.

Unaltered limestone grassland

Apart from the presence of the sugar limestone, the limestone topography of Upper Teesdale differs from that of the Craven area in the relative absence of limestone pavement with clints and grikes. The thick horizontal beds of limestone form low cliffs and although well-jointed are for the most part covered with soils of varying thickness. On some of the outcrops the clint and grike pattern can be seen in the present-day covering of turf. If, as is thought by some, the limestone pavements of Craven are due to

Common Bent — Red Fescue — Heath Bedstraw community (NVC U4)
© Dave Mitchell

loss of an original covering of soil down the grikes, the question arises as to why the soil covering has been preserved in Teesdale? Obviously, whatever the explanation for the different limestone topography of the two areas, there is a problem here for further investigation.

The vegetation of the shallower soils derived directly from the weathering of limestone resembles very much that of the sugar limestone (NVC CG10) with fescues, blue moor-grass and crested hair-grass as the principal grasses associated with harebell, thyme, vernal (spring) sandwort and spring gentian. On the deeper

Common Bent — Sheep's Fescue — Wild Thyme community (NVC CG10)
© Dave Mitchell

soils leaching has started and here bent and fescue are the dominants, associated this time with a corresponding reduction of the lime-loving species; scattered patches of heavily grazed heather and bilberry may also be present. Another very beautiful plant in the turf of these slightly leached soils is the mountain pansy.

Pigott records an interesting variant of this turf from

Fruits of three-flowered rush
© Margaret E Bradshaw

Bird's-eye primrose
© Dave Mitchell

670 m on Mickle Fell, where the soil derived from downwashed drift is flushed by calcareous water. In the close-grazed turf on this soil the lovely alpine forget-me-not *(Myosotis alpestris)* is plentiful, as also are spring gentian, mossy saxifrage *(Saxifraga hypnoides)* and mountain everlasting.

To conclude this section on the grass heath of Teesdale, it must be emphasised that the types described represent, as it were, reference points in an almost continuous range of variation. Many intermediate communities could be described. As we have seen the direction of variation is controlled on the one hand largely by the moisture regime of the soils and on the other by the base-status of the soils. Superimposed on both of these is the grazing factor.

Flush Vegetation

Gravelly and stony flushes

On the sugar limestone area of Widdybank and Cronkley Fells, open, gravelly and stony flushes exist either as sharply defined patches in the surrounding drier vegetation or in an association with a transition through dwarf-sedge marsh to the drier areas. A typical feature of these flushed sites is the occurrence of numerous small knobbly or large dark-green hummocks of the mosses *Hymenostylium recurvirostrum* and *Catoscopium nigritum*; some of these can measure almost 1 m in diameter and may reach a height of 30 cm. In the vicinity of some calcareous streams the hummocks, with the exception of the top 2–3 cm, become encrusted and fused into a porous rock (tufa) by the deposition of calcium carbonate; certain blue-green algae would appear to be active in this deposition.

In more exposed situations the normal hummocks assume a crescent shape and against the concave surfaces to the windward, windblown detritus accumulates forming a small inclined bank. Cushions may also be formed by two other mosses *Palustriella falcata* and *Scorpidium revolvens*.

These wet gravel patches on Widdybank Fell provide the only known habitat in the British Isles for bog sandwort *(Minuartia stricta)* and fortunately for its survival it is an inconspicuous, small plant; other rare and interesting species include the three-flowered rush *(Juncus triglumis)*, yellow saxifrage, alpine meadow-rue, Scottish asphodel, alpine rush and variegated horsetail. butterwort and the yellow sedge, *(Carex lepidocarpa)*, are very characteristic species, too; and the rare British mosses *Amblyodon dealbatus*, *Catascopium nigritum* and *Meesia uliginosa* also contribute to the floristic interest of the gravely flushes.

Brophyte flushes

Where the drainage water is more highly localised within the blanket bogs of the area

Philonotis fontana — Saxifrage stellaris (star saxifrage) community (NVC M32). Inset *Philonotis fontana* and star saxifrage.
© Dave Mitchell

and the higher slopes of the Dun Fells, Mickle Fell and Dufton Fell, nutrient-poor flushes are mostly dominated by the mosses typical of the flush bogs, forming bright-green or reddish-brown spongy carpets (NVC M37). Where the water has a slightly higher mineral content, bog-mosses give way to a variety of other mosses and liverworts such as *Philonotis fontana*, *Dichodontium palustre*, *Warnstorfia exannulata* and *Warnstorfia sarmentosa*. These, also, form spongy cushions, but they are associated with a greater variety of vascular plants, including blinks *(Montia fontana)*, bog stitchwort *(Stellaria alsine)*, opposite-leaved golden-saxifrage *(Chrysosplenium oppositifolium)*, chickweed willowherb *(Epilobium alsinifolium)* and various grasses and sedges. The most outstanding plant of these flushes is the rare, yellow marsh saxifrage *(Saxifraga hirculus)*. This arctic-alpine is centred in Lunedale, Teesdale and Weardale in north England, and has a few records in the Pennines and Scotland and a cluster in Ireland. Other arctic-alpines in these flushes are alpine willowherb *(Epilobium anagallidifolium)*, starry saxifrage *(Saxifraga stellaris)* and hairy stonecrop *(Sedum villosum)*.

To conclude, the vegetation of Upper Teesdale comprises a very large variety of plant communities, where the juxtaposition of the common and the rare makes the scientific importance of the area far greater than the sum of the number of the individual types. It is a truly unique area.

Interest in this flora lies not only in its variety but also because its members belong to diverse geographical elements.

References

Averis, B (2013), *Plant and Habitats.*

Averis, B *et al*, (2004), *An illustrated Guide to British Upland Vegetation*, JNCC.

Other references are listed at the end of Chapter 6.

Chapter 6

Origins and history of the Teesdale flora

Margaret E Bradshaw and Judith Turner

Botanists know the remarkable collection of plants of outstanding scientific interest, referred to in the last chapter, as the 'Teesdale Assemblage'.

The first record to be published was of shrubby cinquefoil *(Potentilla fruticosa)* by John Ray in 1677. This plant had almost certainly been shown to him on the

Five botanists in Upper Teesdale
© Janet Rawlins

The headstone of William Oliver in Middleton-in-Teesdale churchyard
© Margaret E Bradshaw

Mountain avens
© Geoff Herbert

south bank of the River Tees below Thorpe and Egglestone Abbey by Ralph Johnson (1629-95), naturalist and Vicar of Brignall. Studies by Horsman (1995) also show that Johnson knew the wild and remote parts of the upper Dale. In addition to shrubby cinquefoil, he had found northern bedstraw *(Galium boreale)*, alpine bistort *(Persicaria bistorta)*, native rosebay willow-herb *(Chamerion angustifolium)*, spring sandwort *(Minuartia verna)*, starry, mossy and hairy saxifrage *(Saxifraga stellaris, S hypnoides, S. villosum)*, Jacob's ladder *(Polemonium caeruleum)*, alpine bartsia *(Bartsia alpina)*, Scottish asphodel *(Tofieldia pusillum)*, dwarf birch *(Betula nana)* and others. Unfortunately, these records were not made public at the time and much of this knowledge appears to have been lost.

At the end of the eighteenth century, William Oliver, a surgeon trained in Scotland with a knowledge of the Scottish mountain flora, arrived in Teesdale. Working alone, or aided by Binks (a lead miner/and 'simpler'), he made many discoveries or re-discoveries of the Teesdale flora. Fortunately, his association with Harriman was the first step that ensured his discoveries reached the learned members of the Linnean Society of London. The second edition of 'A tour of Teesdale' (Garland 1813) contained a list of over 15 plants, 'which had been supplied by Mr Oliver, a local surgeon'. By the early part of the nineteenth century more species had been found, including spring gentian *(Gentiana verna)*, mountain avens *(Dryas octopetala)*, Teesdale (rock) violet *(Viola rupestris)*, bog stitchwort *(Minuartia stricta)*, bog orchid *(Hammarbya paludosa)* and bearberry *(Arctostaphylos alpinus)*. In his flora, Baines (1840) included these and other members of the 'Assemblage' and a dense paragraph on plants on the

Durham side of the Tees. One famous botanist, visiting Teesdale in 1842, recorded Scottish asphodel, hoary rock-rose *(Helianthemum oelandicum* ssp. *levigatum)*, alpine bartsia, false sedge *(Kobresia simpliciuscula)* and 'several others' – what were these, apparently too well known by those energetic plant hunters that they were not worth listing in his diary? By 1863 Baker, in his Flora, lists at least 22 of the so-called 'Teesdale Assemblage'. Further additions were made so that, almost one hundred years later Pigott (1956) gave some 70 flowering plants and as many lower plants of special phytogeographical interest. Surprisingly, the thrill of discovery in this well-worked area still exists, for in recent years new species have been added, species thought to be extinct have been re-found and other very local plants found in new places.

Many of the species are widely distributed in the arctic and the high mountains of the northern hemisphere, and these belong to the arctic-alpine element, eg. Lady's mantle *(Alchemilla glomerulans)*, alpine bartsia, hair sedge *(Carex capillarum)*, hoary whitlow grass *(Draba incana)*, spring sandwort, alpine bistort, yellow saxifrage *(Saxifraga aizoides)* and alpine meadow-rue *(Thalictrum alpinum)*; the arctic-sub-arctic element is represented by alpine foxtail *(Alopecurus magellanicus)* (arctic foxtail would be more appropriate!) and another Lady's mantle *(Alchemilla wichurae)*; some have their main distribution in the mountains of central Europe and so are the alpine element: spring gentian, mossy saxifrage and alpine penny-cress *(Noccaea caerulescens)*; a northern montane element contains wood crane's-bill *(Geranium sylvaticum)*, bird's eye primrose *(Primula farinosa)* and globeflower *(Trollius europeus)*; others with a continental northern type of distribution in Europe are melancholy

Small scabious

Early spring sedge

Mountain avens

Arctic-Alpine mountain avens, juxtaposed with southern species early spring sedge and small scabious on Cronkley Fell in 2017
© Margaret E Bradshaw

Horseshoe vetch
© Margaret E Bradshaw

thistle *(Cirsium heterophyllum)*, early spring sedge *(Carex ericetorum)* and Teesdale (rock) violet; more unexpected and significant are the continental southern species: hoary rockrose and horseshoe vetch *(Hippocrepis comosa)*. Nowhere else in Britain do these species grow together. This is the real significance of the Teesdale Assemblage — relics of the Late-glacial/early Boreal periods 10/8,000 BC.

The specialness of the interest created by this unusual convergence of so many geographical elements is appreciated when they are considered in the context of the surrounding vegetation which is characterised by such typically west European species as heather or ling, cross-leaved heather, bog asphodel, heath rush and cotton-grass.

The high proportion of arctic-alpine species in the Teesdale flora, the severe climatic features and the significant correlation between some at least of the rare plants and the peculiar metamorphosed 'sugar limestone' led to much speculation on the origin of the assemblage, culminating in the famous discussion at the Royal Society in 1935 (Royal Society, 1935).

Today, it is generally agreed that the majority of the 'Teesdale assemblage of plants' are relics, which were widespread in much of Britain in the Late-glacial period and subsequent warmer periods. Fragmentation of their, then, more or less continuous distribution patterns took place during the subsequent warmer (forest) and later wetter (blanket-bog) periods.

A further special feature of interest exhibited by several of the rarities is that taxonomically they are represented in Teesdale by local races. In some cases, the divergence from other populations of the same species is sufficiently great to warrant their reclassification as a new sub-species. This is so in hoary rockrose, where the Teesdale population is *Helianthemum oelandicum* ssp. *levigatum* (Proctor 1956). Similarly, a Teesdale sub-species of the bitter milkwort *(Polygala amarella)* has been described by Fearn (1971). This species was nearly eliminated from Teesdale by botanists collecting the largest and most floriferous specimens. The plant is known now to be a short-lived perennial and therefore very dependent on successful seed production and germination to maintain the populations. Several species are represented in Teesdale by dwarf or smaller forms: Pigott (1956) points out that some of the Teesdale populations of alpine forget-me-not are much more dwarf than their Ben Lawers counterparts and Elkington (1964) confirms this is

Nowhere else in Britain do these species grow together. This is the real significance of the Teesdale Assemblage genetically controlled; Teesdale mountain avens has very small leaves which are maintained in cultivation; as are the genetic dwarf plants of hoary whitlow grass *(Draba incana* var. *nana)* though these occur in other areas as well as Teesdale. Special studies by Elkington & Woodell (1963) on shrubby cinequefoil again reveal difference in leaf shape between Teesdale and Irish populations and Elkington (1963) also reports differences between the similarly situated populations of spring gentian.

As the Teesdale assemblage of plants exhibits so many special features of interest, it is not surprising that it has excited much interest and speculation as to its origin and history. Wilmot (1930) and Blackburn (1931) suggested that the flora had survived the last main glaciation of Great Britain and perhaps also earlier ones on ice-free areas (nunataks) in the Teesdale uplands and whilst some of the species might well have done so, subsequent research work has shown that ten to twelve thousand years ago many of the characteristic Teesdale plants were widespread in the lowlands of England, Ireland and southern Scotland and for that matter in much of central Europe too. The evidence for this comes from the fossil content of deposits laid down during the late-glacial period. Thus from a late-glacial site at Neasham, near Darlington, Blackburn (1952) identified fossils of mountain avens, hoary rockrose, least willow *(Salix herbacea)* and tea-leaved willow, lesser clubmoss, alpine meadow rue and juniper, all of which, except the willow, occur in Upper Teesdale now and which must in late-glacial times have been constituents of the vegetation of the Darlington lowlands. From a site near London at Nazeing, Allison, Godwin and Warren (1952) identified fossils of shrubby cinquefoil, hoary whitlow grass, mountain avens etc., and pollen of Jacob's ladder and rockrose; while Mitchell (1953) from similar deposits in Ireland has identified seeds of what is probably bog sandwort, now known in Britain only on Widdybank Fell. The position thus is that the fossil remains of practically all the Teesdale rarities have been recovered from late-glacial deposits in this country or on the continent (see Chapter 4).

Some of this late-glacial flora is thought to have immigrated in late-glacial times from further south on the continent, over the dry bed of the southern North Sea or from refuges around our shores, which are now below sea-level, although some, particularly the hardier species, probably survived the glaciation in sheltered places in the ice-free part of southern Britain or even further north on nunataks. However, wherever they actually survived, it is now well established that the Teesdale rarities were widespread in the lowlands of the British Isles during the late-glacial period and so the

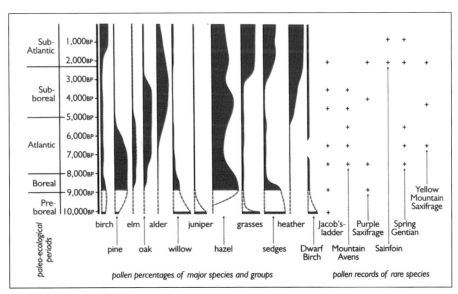

Composite pollen diagram from Cow Green reservoir area, by Dr J Turner, from Scott 2017

interesting question has become, how have they managed to survive the last ten thousand years in Upper Teesdale when elsewhere they died out with the development of the post-glacial forests? We will now consider this question.

There can be no doubt that trees were growing in Upper Teesdale during the post-glacial period as they were elsewhere. This has been demonstrated by pollen-analyses of peat from the area (Johnson and Dunham, 1963, Squires, 1971 and Turner *et al.*, 1973). However, it was no uniform forest (Turner and Hodgson, 1979, 1983, 1991). Even on such exposed summits as Cross

Fell there were trees in mid-post glacial times, though not necessarily forming dense woodland (Turner, 1984). On the higher fells hazel and elm were growing more abundantly than in the valley indicating, as these species do, that the soils there were more fertile than they are today. There was also an area

Whin Sill cliffs open habitat with rock whitebeam, Holwick
© Margaret E Bradshaw

with considerable quantities of pine centred on the basin now occupied by the Cow Green Reservoir. And there must have been plenty of other variations but on too small a scale to be detected by pollen analysis.

This varied woodland was at its most extensive between about seven and eight thousand years ago when peat with its associated plant communities was restricted to a few of the higher cols and to flatter areas just below the ridges where drainage was impeded. Since then blanket peat communities have been replacing woodland more widely, the modern peat profiles often revealing the remains of the earlier trees at or near their base. The blanket peat spread rapidly between about seven and five thousand years ago during a wetter period, known as the Atlantic, and during the last two and a half millennia several factors have interacted to produce the present landscape. There have been further wet periods together with more demand nationwide for timber, sheep grazing, game-shooting and the practice of agriculture. More recently the peat has begun to erode.

Even before there was any evidence from pollen analysis, Godwin (1949), Pigott (1956) and Pigott and Walters (1954) had suggested that the rare plants had survived in the predominantly wooded and peat-covered landscape because there were always a number of open habitats for them, and initially a larger area of limestone and of base-rich soils would have been available. Today it is even easier to envisage this. Most of the rare species are intolerant of shade, some could have survived in the more open woodland on the fell tops, especially adjacent to the small pockets of peat in the cols, where there would have been plenty of light. Some of the rarities would have been at home along the banks of the Tees and beside the many sikes of the area. Large mammals, like bison, bones of which have been found locally, would have helped to maintain open unstable soils by their trampling and browsing especially around water sources. Drier cliff-ledge habitats too would have been available for some of the rarities throughout the forest period and the developing wet valley and blanket peat communities themselves would have supported others.

There is, however, additional evidence for the survival of the rare species because fossil pollen of a surprisingly large proportion of them has now been found in the peat deposits of Cronkley and Widdybank Fells and others, which are now below the waters of the Cow Green Reservoir. Unfortunately, not every species produces diagnostic pollen. For example, rare spring sedge has pollen which cannot be distinguished from that of other sedges, and spring and bog sandworts both produce pollen indistinguishable from that of several other members of the Caryophyllaceae (pink family). But the following rare plants do produce diagnostic pollen: thrift *(Armeria maritima)*, dwarf birch, mountain avens, spring gentian, hoary rockrose, bird's eye primrose, sea plantain, Jacob's ladder, alpine bistort,

Hoary rockrose
© Geoff Herbert

cloudberry *(Rubus chamaemorus)*, least willow *(Salix herbacea)*, mountain saxifrage *(Saxifraga aizoides)*, starry saxifrage, Scottish asphodel and chickweed wintergreen *(Trientalis europaea)*. Of these sixteen species, the pollen of eleven, all except bird's eye primrose, least willow, Scottish asphodel and chickweed wintergreen, has been found in deposits dating from the forest period. As the absence of a fossil pollen record does not, of course, necessarily mean that the plant itself was not growing in the area – insect pollinated plants, such as bird's eye primrose, do not shed into the atmosphere much pollen that could become preserved — this evidence confirms beyond any reasonable doubt that the rare plants did survive in Upper Teesdale during the maximum development of woodland and peat bog.

The fossil pollen evidence, interestingly enough, also supports the idea that some of them have been able to expand considerably during the last two thousand years or so as more suitable habitats have become available. Cloudberry, for example, has increased as more blanket peat has developed. Rockrose has expanded with the increase in grassland and so has sea plantain. Jacob's ladder, which was recorded from Teesdale last century, was at its most abundant when the woodland soils were becoming wetter and going over to blanket peat, which is interesting because today it normally grows in tall herbaceous woodland communities where the soil is damp. Fossil pollen of sainfoin *(Onobrychis viciifolia)* has also been recorded. This is not a member of the Teesdale flora today but it must have been in the past. This is an important addition as the species is a member of the south continental element.

Thus this is good evidence supporting the view that Upper Teesdale has been a refuge for late-glacial plants through the post-glacial period to present times. A few, such as the bog mosses *Sphagnum austinii* and *S. fuscum*, are relics of the wetter Atlantic times, and fortunately have survived the moorland management practices of man. Mysteries remain: in one group *(Alchemilla)* there has been some discussion as to whether the three species of the Continental element *(A. monticola, A. acutiloba, A. subcrenata)* are early post-glacial relics or have been introduced by early human invaders during the last millennia (Bradshaw, 1962). As diagnostic remains do not exist, evidence of their history may have to be sought through archaeology or folk customs. Lady's mantle was

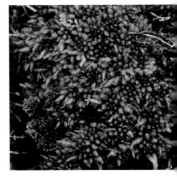

Sphagnum austinii, near Tinkler's Sike, Widdybank Fell
© Margaret E Bradshaw

a herb valued by women who may well have taken seed with them when migrating. Evidence of human occupation in Upper Teesdale since the Late Mesolithic period is provided by chert microliths found on the east shore of Cow Green Reservoir in 2016 close to present day sites of many of the rare species (Young, 2017).

The high incidence of distinct local races in several species can be explained as small-scale evolutionary changes which have taken place during the long isolation of the populations in their Teesdale habitats.

In recent years research has turned to studies of the plant communities. Pigott's first detailed descriptions, published in 1956, have been followed by more detailed investigations of the relationships between the communities and some species and the environmental factors of nutrients, climate, grazing and soil erosion. In addition, studies have been conducted on the population dynamics and reproductive performance of a number of rare species, essential information for determining a management policy for their survival.

A classification of the vegetation of part of the area was completed by Jones in 1973. Using the method of the central European botanists known as phytosociology, Jones found eight classes of vegetation and described several new associations and lesser units, some peculiar to Teesdale. It is of interest to note that the Teesdale rarities tend to occur in the transition zones between the major vegetation classes. Indeed, Jones' work supports the suggestion (Bellamy *et al.*, 1969) that the vegetation in Teesdale, which contains the rare species, constitutes a boundary zone between the arctic/alpine calcareous grasslands of the Elyno-Seslerietea and the Seslerio-Mesobromion, the upland form of the calcareous semidry grassland found in southern Britain and lowland Europe of the class Festuco-Brometea. In Europe these classes meet in the central mountains. The Teesdale peculiarities revealed in the wide range of geographical elements can now be seen in the context of widespread vegetation classes of Europe.

This chapter cannot be closed without reference to the effects of the Cow Green reservoir. As predicted, at least twenty-one acres of unique vegetation were destroyed by the flooding and shore erosion is claiming more. Also destroyed were more acres of common vegetation made scientifically more important because of its juxtaposition with the rare forms. Considerable proportions of the Teesdale populations of several rare species were growing in the reservoir basin: 10% of the rock violet, 40% of the early spring sedge, all the tall bog-sedge *(Carex magellanica)* in this part of Teesdale and considerable quantities of many other rarities: spring gentian, false sedge, alpine rush, bird's eye primrose. The greatest loss was of the vegetation mosaics composed of patches of rare and common plant communities. The finest of these was by Slapestone Sike, where south and northwest faces of opposed slopes in a steep-sided valley provided a unique natural outdoor laboratory not repeated anywhere in Teesdale.

Early spring sedge
© Margaret E Bradshaw

Before inundation the vegetation was described and mapped; herbarium collections were made of the hundred and twenty plants of the reservoir basin for distribution to the major national Herbaria in Europe, Russia and North America; some 15,000 live plants were lifted, most going to centres of research, including two major collections representative of the genetic stock of some twenty species, to be maintained as sources of material at Durham and Manchester Universities, alas both collections have been destroyed. Ironically the opportunity was provided to undertake research which was itself destructive of the rare communities, before the final flooding.

In spite of these losses, Upper Teesdale is still an exciting place in which to do research.

References

Allison, J, Godwin, H & Warren, S H (1952) Late-glacial deposits at Nazeing in the Lea Valley, North London, *Phil.Rans.R.Soc.B*, **236**, 169.

Arnold, S M and Monteith, J L (1974) Plant development and mean temperature in a Teesdale habitat, *J.Ecol.* **62**, 711.

Baker, J G and Tate, G (1868) A New Flora of Northumberland and Durham, *Hist.Trans.of Northumberland and Durham* **11**.

Baines, H (1840) *Flora of Yorkshire*. London.

Bellamy *et al.* (1969), Status of the Teesdale Rarities. *Nature*, **222** pp238-342.

Blackburn, K B (1931), The Late-glacial and Post-glacial periods in the North Pennines. II. Possible survivals in our flora, T*rans. Nth. Nat. Un.* **1**, 32.

Blackburn, K B (1952), The dating of a deposit containing an elk skeleton found at Neasham near Darlington, County Durham. *New Phyt.* **51**, 364.

Bradshaw, M E (1970), 'Teesdale Flora' in Dewdney, J. (ed), Durham County and City with Teesside. *British Association*, Durham.

Bradshaw, M E (1962), The distribution and status of five species of the *Alchemilla vulgaris* L. aggregate, in Upper Teesdale, *J.Ecol.*, **50**, 681.

Elkington, T T (1963), Biological Flora of the British Isles: *Gentiana verna* L. *J.Ecol.*, **51**, 755.

Elkington, T T (1964), Biological Flora of the British Isles: *Myosotis alpestris* F.W. Smidt. L., *J.Ecol.*, **52**, 769.

Elkington, T T (1969), *Potentilla fruticosa* L., *New Phytol.* **68**, 151.

Elkington, T T (1971),Biological Flora of the British Isles: *Dryas octopetala* L. *J.Ecol.*, **69**, 887.

Elkington, T T (1972), Variation in *Gentiana verna* L *New Phytol.*, **71**, 1203.

Elkington, T T & Woodell, S R J (1963), Biological Flora of the British Isles: *Potentilla fruitcosa* L. *J.Ecol.*, **51**, 769.

Fearn, G M (1972), The distribution of interspecific chromosome races of *Hippocrepis comosa* and their phytogeographical significance. *New Phytol.* **71**, 1221.

Godwin, H (1949), The spreading of the British Flora considered in relation to conditions of the Late glacial period. *J.Ecol.*, **37**, 140.

Horseman, F (1995), Ralph Johnson's notebook. *Archives of Natural History.* **22** (2):147-167.

Hutchinson, D W (1971), The experimental alteration of *Kobresia*-rich sward in Upper Teesdale: in Duffy, E, *The Scientific Management of Animals and Plant Communities for Conservation.* London.

Johnson, G A L *et al.* (1971), Unique bedrock and soils associated with the Teesdale flora. *Nature*, **232**, 453.

Johnson, G A L & Durham, K C (1963), *The geology of Moor House*, Nature Conservancy Monograph N°2, HMSO, London.

Jones, A V (1973), *A phytosociological study of Widdybank Fell in Upper Teesdale*, PhD Thesis, University of Durham.

Matthews, J R (1955), *Origin and Distribution of the British Flora.* London.

McVean, D and Radcliffe, D A (1962), 'Plant communities of the Scottish Highlands'. HMSO, London.

Mitchell, G F (1953), Further identifications of macroscopic plant fossils from Irish Quaternary deposits, especially a Late-glacial deposit at Mapastown, Co. Louth. *Proc.R.Ir.Acad.B.* **55**, 221.

Pigott, C D and Walters, S M (1954), On the interpretation of the discontinuous distributions shown by certain British species of open habitats. *J. Ecol.* **42**: 96-116.

Pigott, C D (1956), The vegetation of Upper Teesdale in the North Pennines. *J.Ecol.*,**44**, 545.

Proctor, M C F (1956), Biological Flora of the British Isles: *Helianthemum* Mill. *J.Ecol.*, **44**, 545.

Radcliffe, D A (1959), The vegetation of the Carneddau, North Wales, I: Grasslands, heaths and bogs. *J.Ecol.*, **47**, 371.

Raistrick, A (1931), The Late-glacial and Post-glacial periods in the North Pennines. *Trans.Nth.Nat.Un.*, **1**, 16.

Reid, E M *et al.* (1935), Discussion on the origin and relationship of the British Flora. *Proc.R.Soc.,B.*, **118**, 197.

Squires, R H (1971), Flandrian history of the Teesdale rarities, *Nature*, **229**, 43.

Turner, J, Hewetson, V P, Hibbert, F A, Lowry, K H & Chambers, C (1973), The history of the vegetation and flora of Widdybank Fell and Cow Green reservoir basin, Upper Teesdale, *Phil.Trans.R.Soc.,B.* **265**, 327.

Turner, J and Hodgson, J (1979), Studies in the Vegetational history of the Northern Pennines, I: Variations in the composition of the early-Flandrian forests, *J.Ecol.*,**67**, 629-646.

Turner, J and Hodgson, J (1983), Studies in the Vegetational history of the Northern Pennines, II: Variations in the composition of the mid-Flandrian forests, *J.Ecol.*,**71**, 95-118.

Turner, J and Hodgson, J (1991), Studies in the Vegetational history of the Northern Pennines, IV: Variations in the composition of the late-Flandrian forests and comparisons with those of the early- and mid-Flandrian, *New Phytol.*,**117**, 165-174.

Valentine, D H & Harvey, M J (1961), *Viola rupestris* Schmidt in Britain, *Proc.B.S.B.I.*,**4**, 129.

Wilmott, A J (1930), Contribution a l'etude du peuplement des Isles Britanniques, *Soc. Biogeographie*, **3**, 163.

Young, R (2017), 'The prehistoric archaeology of Teesdale and Weardale: a short overview', in *The Quaternary landscape history of Teesdale and the north Pennines*, ed. D J A Evans, 88-97.

Chapter 7

Fauna

John C Coulson and Ian Findlay

Mammals

Sheep, mostly Swaledale, are the most obvious mammals in Upper Teesdale and graze over much of the open upland areas. Rearing sheep on the uplands was first developed by Cistercian monks several hundred years ago, and this involved the burning of trees and shrubs which were at that time widespread in the uplands and replaced it by 'moorland', a mixture of grassland and heather which produced better grazing. Within the last 200 years, shooting red grouse *(Lagopus lagopus)* became fashionable and many areas of uplands had their management modified to increase the amounts of heather, the main food of adult red grouse. Currently, both sheep and grouse are a source of income and employment in Upper Teesdale and much of the

Roe deer
© Hilary Chambers

area is covered by upland farms and open 'moorland'.

Many of the other mammals of the Upper Dale are inconspicuous or nocturnal. Roe deer *(Capreolus capreolus)* maintain good numbers and are increasing, but fallow deer *(Dama dama)* and red deer *(Cervus elaphus)* only occasionally wander into the area. Hedgehogs *(Erinaceus europaeus)* occur widely in the lower Dale but numbers have suffered over the past 10 years from road-kills. Badgers *(Meles meles)* occur throughout the Dale, up to 600 m, but are mainly restricted to woodland and areas of scrub. Otters *(Lutra lutra)* have made a comeback along the Tees as recorded by Durham Wildlife Trust surveys over the past four years.

Recent mild winters and less snow cover have led to rabbits *(Oryctolagus cuniculus)* becoming widespread, especially where soil allows burrowing, and even on the higher fells. This is exacerbated by low numbers of predators. High rabbit density in areas with deep soils produces in-breeding, with offspring colours varying from brown to brown/white to black (these individuals are not 'pet rabbits' that have been released!) Rabbits cause considerable problems for farmers and their overgrazing can threaten the survival of rare plants — five rabbits can eat as much as one sheep.

Hares are infrequent and rare on the moors. A large increase in mole *(Talpa europaea)* numbers over the past 20 years has created problems for farmers through disruption to grass/hay meadow growth and damage to big bale silage caused by molehill soil.

Surveys in the juniper woodland and other woodland/grassland sites over the last 30 years show steady numbers of short-tailed field vole *(Microtus agrestis)*, bank vole *(Myodes glareolus)* and long-tailed wood mouse *(Apodemus sylvaticus)* but may not show overall abundance. Short-tailed field vole numbers are cyclical. 2015 and 2016 were explosive breeding seasons; abundant populations attract shorteared owls *(Asio flammeus)* to breed.

Bank vole
© Hilary Chambers

Most of the mammalian carnivores, such as fox *(Vulpes vulpes)*, stoat *(Mustela erminea)* and weasel *(Mustela nivalis)* are kept at a low density for the benefit of grey partridge *(Perdix perdix)*, red grouse *(Lagopus lagopus)* and black grouse *(Tetrao tetrix)* and there is evidence that this management favours numbers of lapwing *(Vanellus vanellus)*, golden plover *(Pluvialis apricaria)*, snipe *(Gallinago gallinago)* and curlew *(Numenius arquata)*.

Common shrew *(Sorex araneus)* is restricted to grasslands, with its main food, earthworms, restricted to mineral soils. Pygmy shrew *(Sorex minutus)* is even more abundant and occurs wherever there are peat soils. It was only within the last 50 years that it was discovered that it occurred commonly on moorlands and has an unusual distribution in England, mainly occurring in conifer woodlands, on sand dunes and areas of deep peat on the

Water vole
© Andrew Ramsay

Whiskered and pipistrelle bats
© Noel Jackson

uplands; all areas with no or few earthworms and where the common shrew as a competitor does not occur. Both common and pygmy shrew have been found living on the summit of Great Dun Fell and this begs the question of how they survive during the winter since they do not hibernate and need to consume invertebrates every few hours. The ground on the fell tops during the winter is often frozen solid for weeks on end and how the shrews find food is unknown. One possibility is that at this time of year they retreat into places where there are deep and unfrozen burrows made by moles. A third shrew species, the water shrew *(Neomys fodiens)* occurs along the banks of the River Tees and its tributaries, although it is rarely reported. Repeated surveys from 2001 have reported good breeding numbers of water vole *(Arvicola amphibious)* on the banks of rivers, becks and sikes, but heavy rainfall in exposed areas in more recent years has washed out many breeding sites.

Middleton-in-Teesdale is home to good numbers of all nine species of bat found in County Durham; whiskered/Brandt's *(Myotis mystacinus / Myotis brandtii)*, Daubenton's *(Myotis daubentonii)*, noctules *(Nyctalus noctula)*, common pipistrelles *(Pipiestrellus pipistrellus)* and soprano pipistrelles *(Pipiestrellus pygmaeus)* are relatively common. The former Field Study Centre in Middleton, monitored by Durham Bat group since 1983, was an important nursery roost for whiskered bats until recently. Bats are scarcer up the Dale, but forage to Langdon Beck where Daubenton's bats and common pipistrelles have been recorded. There a brown long-eared bat *(Plecotus auritus)* roost at Bowlees Visitor Centre in the past. Newbiggin has an important colony of whiskered/Brandt's bats that moves between the former chapel and other buildings, possibly from a local nursery roost. The highest known roost is at Dent Bank where both brown long-eared and common pipistrelles breed.

The major importance of Upper Teesdale to bats is in late summer when the blooming heather is buzzing with insects. Bats follow the becks to the high moors to fatten up ready for hibernation in caves, adits and mines. Concerted work has shown that Moking Hurth, Elf Cleugh Cave, Swinhope Cave and Swinhope Mine provide a winter home for Brandt's, whiskered, Daubenton's, brown long-eared and Natterer's bats *(Myotis nattereri)*.

Birds

The Dale has a large number of bird species recorded, many breeding, but most leave the area in winter, the notable exceptions being the two grouse species. Woodlands at lower altitudes have the expected mixture of small birds breeding, including the smallest British bird, the goldcrest *(Regulus regulus)* which has a preference for conifer plantations. Garden warblers *(Sylvia borin)* and willow warblers *(Phylloscopus trochilus)* continue to increase in number, but wood warbler *(Phylloscopus sibilatrix)* and tree pipit *(Anthus trivialis)* have disappeared during the last five to eight years. Within the last 50 years the Dale has lost two breeding bird species: corncrake *(Crex crex)* and dotterel *(Charadrius morinellus)*, while twite *(Linaria flavirostris)*, a small finch, only just manages to hangs on as a breeding species. In recent years four new species have been recorded as breeding: oystercatcher *(Haematopus ostralegus)*, goosander *(Mergus merganser)*, jackdaw *(Corvus monedula)* and ringed plover *(Charadrius hiaticula)*.

Black grouse, male at lek
© Hilary Chambers

Black grouse
© Keith Robson

Black Grouse

Black grouse is perhaps the rarest English breeding bird in the Dale. Numbers, monitored annually, plummeted after the bad winters of 1976 to 1987, but a slow population recovery since then is largely attributed to more open winters and milder conditions. These birds form leks in the Dale. These sites, used yearly, are places where males collect within a small area in the spring to display to and attract females as mates. One lek is visible from the road running from Forest-in-Teesdale to St John's Chapel in Weardale.

Waders

Ten species of breeding waders, and one uncommon visitor, are highly conspicuous and form a major feature of Upper Teesdale. The Dale must rate within the top six to eight sites for breeding waders in Great Britain. No cereal or root crops are grown, but moorland, hay meadows, pastures and allotments provide a good mixture of breeding habitats for these birds.

Weather patterns have changed over the past 20 years; winters have been more open, with less snow cover over a shorter period of time on middle and higher ground. In recent years waders have returned to the Dale two to four weeks earlier, congregating on major sites as their numbers build up. Such sites record high numbers of species; lapwing (400 – 600), curlew (20 – 60+), golden plover (100 – 200), redshank (20), common snipe (20 – 30), oystercatcher (60 – 80). If the weather is settled, the birds disperse to their primary breeding sites, sometimes by late March. But they will return temporarily to their mustering areas if snow falls again. Surprisingly, 20 to 30 skylark may join them.

Lapwing

Lapwings are the most numerous wader and many breed in the upland pastures and hay meadows, particularly those without nearby trees which would be used by crows as lookouts for finding their nests. Occasionally pairs breed on Cross Fell. Despite national declines, lapwing numbers still remain high in the Dale and continue to be the subject of long-term research. Following a period of hard winters, 1976 to 1986, the lapwing numbers increased greatly in the springs of 1987 to 1990. Very high numbers, with a spill-over from primary to secondary sites, were also recorded in 2007 and 2016, possibly due to milder winters.

Many of the young birds reared in the Dale return to breed very close to where they had hatched and often in the same field, but a few individuals move much further, with one ringed chick being found east of

Lapwing
© Anne Kelly

Golden Plover in flight
© David Williams

Moscow during a later breeding season. Early return in late February/early March and early nesting, before the ground has warmed up, risks food shortage — only one or two chicks surviving in the first brood.

Golden Plover

Golden plovers breed on the high fells above 400 m and on bogs, and in the breeding season follow walkers for considerable distances, giving their plaintive alarm calls. Calcium levels are low in their food on the acid moors and pairs regularly fly in the evenings to limestone areas at lower altitudes to consume snails, presumably to allow the female to accumulate the calcium needed for egg-shell production. Breeding numbers have not fluctuated over the past 46 years — 66 active nest sites have been recorded annually, with a variation of only four to six around this figure each year.

Golden Plover
© Hilary Chambers

Dunlin

Dunlin *(Caldris alpina)* are the smallest and rarest wader in the Dale with between eight and 16 scattered pairs breeding on the top of the high fells.

Curlew

Curlew breed on the lower moors and in rough pasture. They are conspicuous because of their size and aerial display flights, while their bubbling calls gives them their common name and their long, down-curved beaks make them readily identifiable. Breeding numbers were never high in the past but, unlike the national decline, curlew have enjoyed very good breeding seasons over the

Curlew
© Hilary Chambers

past three years. A late snowfall in March 2008 pushed waders down from the upper Dale, but more than 120 curlew remained, their long shanks and probing bills coping well with the deep snow.

Common Snipe

Common snipe are widespread on wet and boggy ground and difficult to see except when making their aerial displays, males repeatedly diving and vibrating two stiff tail feathers which produce a buzzing or drumming sound and reveals the presence of this otherwise secretive species. Breeding numbers fluctuate with high or low numbers from year to year.

Snipe
© Anne Kelly

Common Sandpiper

Common sandpiper *(Actitis hypoleucos)* is a migratory species restricted to the streams and edges of reservoirs and are readily recognised in flight, which involves several wing beats followed by a brief glide, or by their bobbing action as they walk along the stream edge and move from rock to rock. Surveys show a constant level of breeding populations.

Oystercatcher with chicks
© Hilary Chambers

Oystercatcher

Oystercatchers have invaded the Dale over the last 50 years, with breeding flocks of 80 to 100 in the last 20 to 30 years. Formerly only coastal nesters, they have spread inland along rivers in northern England and now nest in streamside fields and on gravel banks. This large and conspicuous black and white wader with red legs and bill engages in noisy piping displays that often involve a small group of individuals. It is a late breeder, usually raising two chicks.

Woodcock

Woodcock *(Scolopax rusticola)* mostly breed in upland woodlands. More recently a few nests have been seen on the high fells, moorland edge and among bracken (possibly due to open winters and less snow cover). They are infrequently seen except when the males become active near sunset, flying at tree canopy height like large bats and repeatedly patrolling back and forth in search of females. It is the only wader species that does not form lasting pairs while breeding and only the female takes care of the young.

Woodcock
© John Miller

Common Redshank

Common redshank *(Tringa totanus)* breeds on wet and marsh areas on farmland and is also noisy when protecting its breeding site, eggs and young. The double or triple alarm call is characteristic, as is the white and brown pattern when in flight and red legs. Records show mixed breeding seasons, good years then bad, for no apparent reason. 2016 was a very good year throughout the Dale.

Redshank
© David Williams

Ringed Plover

Ringed plover had previously been restricted to a few coastal nesting sites in County Durham but have recently invaded Upper Teesdale and a few now breed around the edges of the reservoirs.

Dotterel

Dotterel used to breed on the main fell tops, but now visit in small numbers only on spring, and sometimes on autumn, passage to and from more northern breeding sites. They sometime occur in small flocks known as 'trips' and the birds are noted for their tameness and the ease with which they can be approached.

Ducks

Few ducks breed in Upper Teesdale. Mallard *(Anas platyrhynchos)* is a fairly common breeding species, with large numbers overwintering and feeding in the fields and, in recent years, in sheep troughs. There were very few wigeon *(Anas penelope)* or teal *(Anas crecca)* pairs before 1980 and small numbers now nest in most years. The building of the Cow Green reservoir has encouraged a few fish-feeding goosanders to breed in the area on the Tees and Maize becks. Merganser *(Mergus serrator)* is a rare visitor, with only one breeding record (in the 1990s). Shelduck *(Tadorna tadorna)* pass over the area each summer on migration from Morecambe Bay and across the North Sea to the Heligoland Bight, where they moult their feathers and remain flightless until new feathers have grown and they then return to England.

Birds of prey

Kestrel *(Falco tinnunculus)* and merlin *(Falco columbarius)* breed in low numbers in the upper Dale. Buzzard *(Buteo buteo)*, peregrine *(Falco peregrinus)* and raven *(Corvus corax)* are present every season but fail to breed. Peregrine falcons are known to have bred previously in a few places in Upper Teesdale. Golden eagle *(Aquila chrysaetos)* and osprey *(Pandion haliaetus)* have occasionally been seen in the Dale, but neither breed here, while a few red kite *(Milvus milvus)* have spread into the area from a reintroduction programme near Gateshead. Hen harrier *(Circus cyaneus)* is rarely seen.

Buzzard
© David Williams

Other species

Different species of small, perching birds breed on the moorland and in the wooded areas of the Dale. Meadow pipit *(Anthus pratensis)* is the commonest small bird on the moorland, while both skylark *(Alauda arvensis)* and yellow wagtail *(Motacilla flava)* occur in decreasing numbers in the meadows. Wheatear *(Oenanthe oenanthe)* and small numbers of ring ouzel *(Turdus torquatus)*, the 'upland blackbird' with a white crescent on the breast, breed on the edges of the moorland where there are stone walls and mineral soils, but they generally avoid the extensive peatlands. Dippers *(Cinclus cinclus)* feed by swimming underwater in the streams to catch aquatic insects, while grey wagtail *(Motacilla cinerea)*, which despite its name has yellow under parts and should not be confused with the yellow wagtail, is restricted to capturing insects which have recently emerged from the streams. Kingfisher *(Alcedo atthis)* is absent from most of the area.

Dipper
© Keith Robson

Black-headed gulls *(Chroicocephalus ridibundas)* breed in the Dale and they nest in varying numbers alongside the upland reservoirs and small ponds. Some of their eggs are legally collected each year under an annual licence issued by Natural England and based on ancient traditional rights to do so. Common gulls *(Larus canus)* are increasing in the winter.

Some bird species are declining in the Dale. Wheatears are fewer, but still widespread as are the yellow and pied wagtails *(Motacilla alba)*. Cuckoo *(Cuculus canorus)* still occurs but in reduced numbers and does not follow its main host, the meadow pipit, onto the moorland as far or as extensively as it used to do.

Adder © Tom Gledhill

Reptiles

Small numbers of adders *(Vipera berus)* occur in the lower woods, scrub areas and on the edge of the moorland and the viviparous lizard *(Lacerta vivipara)* is widespread over the moorland areas and individuals are sometimes found sunning themselves on sunny days.

Amphibians

Frogs *(Rana temporaria)* are incredibly abundant, and spawn in pools on mineral soils almost to the highest parts of the Dale, but they do not use pools on blanket bog. Spawning in the spring is later than at lower altitudes and growth of the tadpoles is slightly slower, with a few even overwintering as tadpoles. Smooth newts *(Triturus lissotriton vulgaris)* and common toads *(Bufo bufo)* occur only in the lower areas of the Dale.

Fish

Fish are reported upon in Chapter 8.

Invertebrates

Sexton (burying) beetle infested on its head with mites
© Lesley Hodgson

Many of the interesting vertebrates living in Upper Teesdale are dependent on numerous invertebrates for food and many of these are abundant, with over 1,400 species recorded. Many insects are numerous, but the most abundant invertebrates are small, thread-like pot worms *(Enchytraeidae)* with over 200,000 and 3 million microscopic nematodes having been recorded in a square metre of upland soil, together with 80,000 springtails, 30,000 mites and 300 spiders. These small, but abundant, animals are the starting point of important food chains for larger invertebrates, such as beetles, true flies, harvestmen and spiders which, in turn, are key food sources for many of the vertebrates. The abundance of the invertebrates cannot be exaggerated and in simple terms for each sheep seen on the uplands in summer, there are tens times their weight of invertebrates hidden in the soils. Some of these invertebrates are extremely rare elsewhere in England and several have been described as species new to science. They all play an important role, along with sheep and fungi, in decomposing all of the annual production of grass on mineral soils, but they fail to do so on the peat areas because of the low nutrient quality of *Sphagnum* and cotton grass and this results in about ten percent of the annual production of plant material produced on the blanket bog remaining and being accumulated as peat.

Unlike many areas of the Arctic, blood-sucking mosquitoes are absent from the moorland, but there are other blood-sucking flies in the Dale. The most irritating are the very small biting midges known scientifically as *Culicoides* or commonly as no-see-ums (and other unrepeatable names used by local people) and these make themselves known to visitors on the few warm days with little wind between April to October. Several species of the blood-sucking blackflies (also called buffalo gnats and not to be confused with the aphids of the same name which occur on plants), and their larvae, live in the fast flowing streams. The small adults suck the blood of birds and mammals and some species take blood from humans and some fly many kilometres to obtain a blood meal. In June and July, the larger horseflies can also common and even more readily attempt to obtain a blood meal from people.

Emperor moth caterpillar
© Fal Sarker

Cranefly
© Chris Lawrence

Violet ground beetle
© Lesley Hodgson

In contrast to the distribution of rare plant species in Upper Teesdale, the areas of deep peat and the fast flowing streams which lie at the head of Teesdale hold almost all of the rare invertebrate species which occur in the Dale and very few are associated with sugar limestone. Because of this difference, many of the zoological studies in the Dale have centred on the higher ground of the Moor House National Nature Reserve, which lies to the south and west of the River Tees, starting at the river's source between Cross Fell and Little Dun Fell. This reserve is an area mainly dominated by deep, blanket bog and wet flushes which rarely dry out because it has a high rainfall and low temperatures throughout the year, producing a climate comparable to many sub-Arctic and tundra areas of northern Europe and also with Iceland at sea-level.

A major reason for the high diversity of invertebrates in the Dale is the wide range of soil types, ranging from deep organic blanket peats through shallow peaty heaths, to rich brown earth mineral soils. These soils have very different invertebrate faunas and this difference makes an appreciable contribution to the high diversity found in the Dale. A second factor is the high rainfall which keeps the ground wet or moist for much of the time and which is appreciably higher at the higher altitudes and this is important because many of the invertebrate animals are small and run a high risk of dehydration. Annual rainfall at Moor House (550 m) is three times greater than at Durham City, while the frequent mists and drizzle results in precipitation falling for ten times longer. These differences, combined with the lower temperatures, result in the soil and peat rarely drying out and so permit the abundance of many small animal species which are unable to exist at lower altitudes.

Invertebrate fauna of grassland and peatland habitats

Upland grasslands

These consist mainly of alluvial soils alongside streams and restricted areas where limestone is at or near the surface and produces rich mineral soils. Peat does not accumulate on these areas because the whole annual production of vegetation is decomposed or is washed away by frequent floods. The invertebrate species are typical of those also found on lowland grasslands and few are nationally rare.

Upland blanket peat

Upland blanket peat has a metre or more of peat which has accumulated since the last Ice Age. This peat is nutrient-poor as the depth of peat prevents the roots of plants from reaching the underlying mineral sub-soil and so has a vegetation restricted to those plant species which can live under these nutrient-poor and waterlogged conditions and are dominated by heather, cotton grass and *Sphagnum* moss. These areas resemble the tundra of Arctic and sub-Arctic areas and which also naturally lack trees and often contain the same invertebrate species. Thus on the blanket bog and the stream side grasslands, two very different faunas exist side by side, one associated with temperate grasslands and the other with arctic areas.

Northern Heaths

These are areas where heather is abundant, but there is little or no peat and the soils are mainly mineral with only small pockets of shallow peat. These are usually at a lower altitude and have been called Northern Heaths and were forested until cleared for sheep grazing, and are now regularly burnt to encourage short heather for red grouse or in a few places more heavily burnt to increase grass for sheep grazing. Cessation of regular burning results in the re-establishment of trees. As a result, these areas are a man-made habitat and have not yet developed their own natural fauna and so are species-poor. Many of the insect species present require and pass part of their lifecycle in sheep dung.

The invertebrates found on these three main habitat types are very different. Earthworms are abundant on the mineral grassland soils and occur at up to 400 under a square metre of ground. In contrast, earthworms are totally absent on blanket bog and few exist on heaths. The role of major invertebrates on blanket bogs are replaced by the larvae (often called leather jackets) of crane-flies *(Tipulidae)* (daddy-long-legs) and these can occur as hundreds of larvae per square metre and 69 species have been recorded at Moor House.

As many of the insects occurring on the blanket bog are northern species and presumably evolved in cold areas of the world where the short summers are only long enough to permit a maximum of one generation each year, the insects almost all pupate and emerge as adults in response to the spring rise in temperature or the lengthening day. Using environmental cues occurring later in the year runs the risk of winter conditions returning before they reach adulthood. As a result, there is a remarkable synchronised emergence of insects on both the arctic tundra and on the blanket bog in Upper Teesdale and most of the individuals are three species of craneflies. Only one of these has been given a common name and has been called the 'grouse fly' because it is eaten in large numbers by young red grouse. It is small, black, has reduced wings, cannot fly and its scientific name is *Molophilus ater*, it occurs at up to a thousand individuals to the square metre. The other species are *Tipula subnodicornis*, a larger species and only the males can fly and *Tricyphona immaculata*, where both sexes are able to fly only short distances. The emergence at the end of May and in the first half of June is a period of superabundance of surface-active insects on the blanket bog, but since none of these species feed as adults they, like mayflies, live for only a few days. Yet at the peak of emergence the blanket bog shimmers as the adults crawl over the heather on a sunny day in search of mates or to lay eggs, but this is soon followed by a paucity of active invertebrates on the blanket bog until the next generation of adults a year later. The pattern of abundance of invertebrates, including craneflies, on blanket peat is shown in Figure 1.

In many cases the grasslands along upland streams, only a few metres from blanket bog, show a very different pattern of invertebrate activity during the year. This mainly involves different species, and insects use different cues as to when to pupate. The peak of craneflies is in August and is due to the emergence of the common cranefly *(Tipula paludosa)* which is also abundant on lowland grasslands and often flies into houses in the autumn. There is no major spring abundance of invertebrates on the grasslands (Figure 2).

As a result of the abundance of heather on Northern Heaths it might be expected to have a similar invertebrate fauna to blanket bog, but this is not so. Craneflies are scarce, apart from the emergence of *Tipula marmorata* in September — a species whose larvae feed on mosses and is also common in the lowlands. Many of the insects recorded on these heaths are species associated with

Blanket bog

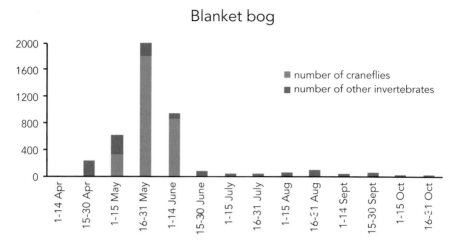

Figure 1: The numbers of invertebrates emerging from a square metre of ground on blanket bog in two-weekly periods from April to the end of October. No captures were made from November to March. No earthworms were present in the soil.

Upland grassland

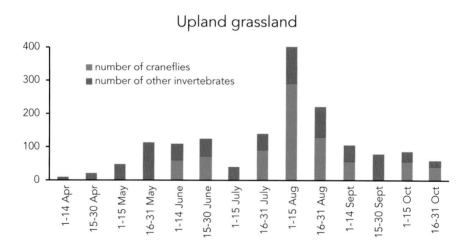

Figure 2: The captures of invertebrates from a square metre of ground at two-week intervals on upland grassland at Moor House from April to the end of October. Note the reduced scale compared to Figure 1 and the much later peak of captures which were all different species to those on blanket bog. Earthworms are not included but were present throughout.

Northern heath

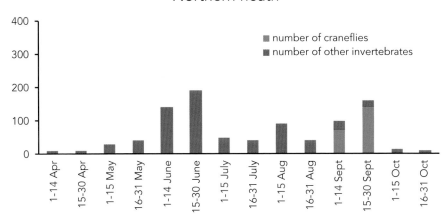

Figure 3: The numbers of active invertebrates per square metre on a northern heath in Upper Teesdale. Note the change of scale. Numbers of captures are much lower than on the blanket bog and upland grassland sites. They involve few rare species and were spread out through the late spring, summer and early autumn. Earthworms were uncommon in the soil throughout the year.

Craneflies and young meadow pipits

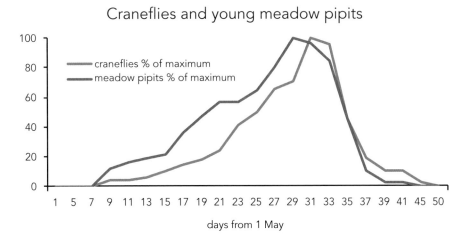

Figure 4: The co-incidence of the emergence of adult craneflies on blanket bog and the numbers of young meadow pipits in nests at Moor House.

dung and if there are no sheep grazing these areas, they would have an even lower diversity. There is only a minor peak of invertebrates in the spring (Figure 3).

The seasonal abundance of invertebrates, and particularly of insects, is important to the success of many of the bird species breeding on the blanket bogs of Upper Teesdale. They are consumed by young wading birds, such as golden plover and curlew, by red grouse and meadow pipits and it is important that these birds breed at a time when this abundant food is available for their chicks, because the periods before and after are times when food is scarce. The close link between the period that the meadow pipit have young in the nest is closely correlated with the peak of emergence of insects on the blanket peat (see Figure 4) and it is evident that the eggs in this species are mainly laid about two weeks before the major emergence takes place. Presumably the birds, like the insects, are responding to the rise in temperature rather than identifying the start of pupation by insects.

The abundance of food on the blanket bog at this time of year is remarkable and one pair of meadow pipits repeatedly walked in a small circle about 2 m radius from the nest collecting craneflies to feed to their chicks and not having to fly to suitable feeding areas. Although the meadow pipit is claimed to rear two broods each year, only a few produce a second brood in Upper Teesdale and while these young are in the nest there is very little food available on the peat areas and they are fed almost exclusively on insects emerging from or alongside the streams, with some adults nesting on the blanket peat flying up to 2 km to collect food for the nestlings.

In contrast to the meadow pipit, the recently-hatched young of wading birds which all have well developed legs on hatching, are frequently led by their parents to suitable feeding grounds. Common sandpiper chicks are almost always led down-stream and the headwaters of the Tees is rapidly emptied of these birds. Adult woodcock are reputed to fly, carrying a chick between their thighs, and to take them past obstructions to reach good feeding areas, but this does not seem to have been observed in Teesdale.

Rarer invertebrates

Only one rare species has been recorded, in the Cow Green area — the round-mouthed whorl snail *(Vertigo genesii)*, discovered in 1979 on Widdybank Fell. This very small snail is a glacial relict which was widespread following the last glaciation, but this is the first time it has been recorded in England in recent times. In contrast, at least five species of invertebrates new to science and four found for the first time in England (including a species of flea) have been found on the higher areas of blanket peat forming the Moor House National Nature Reserve. Some taxonomic groups are represented by many species in Upper Teesdale. A total of 157 species of rove beetles and 69 species of craneflies have been found and identified from Moor House and more must exist at lower altitudes in Upper Teesdale.

The streams contain the nymphs of several interesting insects, such as the rare stoneflies *Capnia vidua* and *Protonemoura montana* and the mayfly *Ameletus inopinatus*, all of which have a very restricted distribution to upland areas in Britain. Some upland pools have the predatory nymphs of the large common hawker dragonfly *(Aeshna juncea)* and large red damselfly *(Pyrrhosoma nymphula)* and a few have the remarkable larvae of the cranefly *(Phalacrocera replicata)*, which in colour and shape closely resemble pieces of *Sphagnum* moss.

Apart from the flowering of thyme in July and heather in August, there are relatively few flowering plants on the blanket peat areas and this is reflected in only one common bee species, *Bombus jonellus*, being widely distributed and there are few other insect species in the area which rely on nectar and pollen as a food source.

Nightly trapping of moths over the past 44 years has recorded over 200 species of macro moth. April to September are the most prolific months with up to ten species caught each night including Hebrew character *(Orthosia gothica)*, large yellow underwing *(Noctua pronuba)*, silver Y *(Autographa gamma)* and July highflyer *(Hydriomena furcata)*. Fewer moths fly in the winter: November moth *(Epirrita dilutata)*, December moth *(Poecilocampa populi)* and winter moth *(Operophtera fagata)* are examples.

The common moths which occur on the wet, high altitude moors are restricted to those which pupate on vegetation above the ground and so avoid the wet, waterlogged soils. The beautiful emperor moth *(Saturnia pavonia)* and northern eggar *(Lasiocampa callunae)* are both large, day-flying moths whose larvae feed mainly on heather and which occur on the high moors. Strangely, the emperor moth can complete its life-cycle in a year, but the northern eggar takes two years, despite both species often occurring together and using the same larval food. Further, the latter species fluctuates dramatically in numbers from year to year, while numbers of the Emperor are much more consistent. The most abundant moth on the moorlands is the

Large yellow underwing
© Keith Robson

minute rush moth *(Coleophora alticolella)*. The larvae feed on the seed capsules of the Moor Rush and the distribution of the moth fluctuates and this is determined by the variable altitude at which the rush sets seed each year. Many will have seen the small silk case produced by the caterpillar protruding from the seed capsules and not recognised these as containing a moth caterpillar. Interestingly, the rush has been setting seed at higher altitudes in recent years and the moth has spread to altitudes over 600 m in some recent years, but every now and again, the rush fails to set seed above a lower altitude, and the caterpillars hatching from eggs laid at the higher levels starve and as a result the moth is again restricted to lower altitudes. In effect it is a biological game of 'snakes and ladders' and offers an insight into how climate variations can directly affect a plant and as a consequence, an insect which feeds on its seeds.

Common blue
© Keith Robson

July highflyer
© Keith Robson

Butterflies are poorly represented and become even less common as one proceeds up the Dale, but these are occasionally increased by migratory species such as painted lady *(Vanessa cardui)* visiting from the continent. A butterfly transect at 300 m, part of a national monitoring programme, has been surveyed between April and September for over 40 years. Sixteen species have been recorded in one year, green veined white *(Pieris napi)* being most abundant and with two broods per season. Good numbers of red admiral *(Vanessa atalanta)*, peacock *(Aglais io)* and small white *(Pieris rapae)* have been recorded, moderate counts of small heath *(Coenonympha pamphilus)* and less of common blue *(Polyommatus icarus)*. Large white *(Pieris brassicae)*, comma *(Polygonia c-album)*, small skipper *(Thymelicus sylvestris)* and small copper *(Lycaena phlaeas)* are rarely recorded. Small tortoiseshell *(Aglais urticae)* has declined in recent years, but dark green fritillary *(Argynnis algaja)* and ringlet *(Aphantopus hyperantus)* have rapidly increased over the past six years. Orange tip *(Anthocharis cardamines)* can be common.

Chapter 8

Freshwater life

**Martyn G Kelly, Trevor D Crisp*, Ben Lamb
and Brian Whitton**

Introduction

Without the River Tees there would be no Teesdale and
so, whilst much of the attention in this book is focussed
on the plant and animal life in the fields and fells, we
should not ignore either the river or the numerous
tributary streams that feed it. Cow Green Reservoir, too,
plays an important part in the story of Upper Teesdale,
not just because of the ways in which it has altered the
landscape and habitats in the upper valley, but also
because the decision to impound the river precipitated
many significant ecological studies and, ironically,
raised the profile of the Teesdale rarities beyond a small
band of botanical cognoscenti.

The River Tees was the first British River to receive a
detailed biological survey (by Butcher and colleagues

* deceased

in the mid-1930s). This was followed in the 1970s and 1980s by studies of the upper reaches of the main river and its tributaries by Durham University and the Freshwater Biological Association (later Institute of Freshwater Ecology and now Centre for Ecology and Hydrology). Since the previous edition of this book, further studies have investigated a wide range of factors including gravel, heavy metals, availability of salmonid spawning habitat and water colour.

The upper tributaries of the Tees range from torrential streams, fed at times of peak flow mainly by surface run-off, to calcareous streams with some or much of their water from limestone springs. Those with the most water from springs are the ones which vary least in flow and have the highest calcium concentrations. The drier the weather the higher the calcium concentration of water in the upper Tees, which can reach 30 mg/litre or more, and can be considered to be 'hard', whereas in wet weather the concentration may fall well below 10 mg/litre and thus considered 'soft' (see Table 1).

Substance	Inflow	Outflow
Calcium	3.50 - 37.2	6.40 - 8.90
Magnesium	0.39 - 1.75	0.60 - 0.90
Sodium	2.10 - 3.96	2.40 - 2.88
Potassium	0.24 - 1.47	0.30 - 0.44
Chloride	3.00 - 5.00	4.20 - 4.90
Sulphate	7.20 - 16.30	7.80 - 10.20
Nitrate-nitrogen	0.00 - 0.15	0.09 - 0.16

Table 1: Range of concentration (mg/litre) of selected chemical susbstances in the River Tees at the inflow and outflow of Cow Green reservoir. For each substance the range of values observed between April 1975 and March 1976 is shown. Note that the reservoir evens out the fluctuation (from Crisp, 1977).

The Tees is unusual amongst British rivers in being comparatively large at a relatively high altitude (550 m). It has a steep headwater slope and is extremely flashy. Butcher *et al.* (1937) noted that at times the rise in water level was so rapid that the flood resembled a tidal wave and the first waters of a spate are very turbid. This wave was known locally as 'the roll' and it was generated by rapid snow melt or severe downpours following longer periods of dry weather. The severity of the spates has been reduced somewhat by the reservoirs in Baldersdale and Lunedale, and since the construction of Cow Green reservoir the wave has not occurred. Nonetheless, the Tees in spate is still spectacular.

Algae

The algae form a large, but often neglected, part of the biodiversity of Britain and Ireland, accounting for about three quarters of all the photosynthetic species. The extent of the diversity of Upper Teesdale streams is illustrated by a survey of a single 10 m length of Harwood Beck in 1992 to 1993 (Kelly, 2006). Four visits to the site over the course of the year yielded between 16 and 45 species per visit, with a total of 70 species in an area of about 90 m² of the stream bed. Diatoms (Bacillariophyta) represented the greatest number of species, but green algae (Chlorophyta) and blue-green algae (Cyanobacteria) were also well represented. In addition there was one record of a freshwater red alga (*Audouinella hermannii*).

The blue-green algae of Upper Teesdale are of particular interest because of their prominence in the upper part of streams combining drainages from limestone and peat-rich soil. Slapestone and Red Sikes are the best places to see these algae. Unlike the nuisance species of lowland lakes and reservoirs, the Teesdale species dominate in water with very low nutrient concentrations for much of the year. *Rivularia* forms dark-green or brownish hemispherical colonies which range from 1 mm to about 2 cm on the upper surface of pebbles and small rocks. Another species, *Schizothrix lardacea*, forms reddish mats on the stream bed and may partly explain how Red Sike got its name. Colonies of another blue-green alga, *Nostoc commune*, are often intermingled with mosses at the edge of the calcareous streams. Both *Nostoc* and *Rivularia* can fix atmospheric nitrogen and so are less dependent on dissolved nitrogen in the water.

Microscopic view of filaments of the cyanobacterium *Rivularia* from Sand Sike, Upper Teesdale. The light-coloured cell at the base of each filament is a heterocyst, responsible for nitrogen fixation. The base of each filament is approximately 10 micrometres (= 1/100th of a millimetre) in diameter.
© Martyn Kelly

The ecology of these organisms has been studied by Brian Whitton and co-workers from the University of Durham over a number of years. *Rivularia* and other blue-green algae in the region use the phosphorus in organic compounds formed by the breakdown of peat (Livingstone & Whitton, 1984). This may explain their abundance in the uppermost stretches of streams where there is a good supply of this from peat drainage. Whilst concentrations of dissolved phosphorus in the calcareous streams are normally very low (often less than 1 mg/litre), there are short periods, especially during early spring, when organic phosphorus is much higher, sometimes reaching concentrations over 1 mg/litre for short periods. When this happens, the *Rivularia* colonies release filaments which glide over the surface of the rock and then aggregate to form new colonies. These can often be seen in May as tiny, almost black, spots.

The Freshwater Biological Association collected samples of phytoplankton — the algae suspended in the water — after the dam closed in June 1970 (Atkinson, 1998). Since then the phytoplankton has been dominated by diatoms, which are characterised by beautifully sculpted cases of silica known as frustules. The first found to be common was *Tabellaria flocculosa* var. *flocculosa*, which is also common in the surrounding streams and pools. This and other early colonists were probably washed into the reservoir from the catchment, whereas later arrivals such as *Aulacoseira italica* were probably introduced in other ways such as on the feet of birds. Phytoplankton other than diatoms which have been recorded include the blue-green alga *Oscillatoria* (now recognised as *Planktothrix*), desmids and colonies of the green alga *Sphaerocystis*.

Desmids are not just found in the plankton of Cow Green reservoir. Boggy pools, such as those beside the Pennine Way between Widdy Bank Farm and the bottom of Cauldron Snout, are also rich habitats for this large group of algae which are most abundant in soft water and acidic habitats. Desmids are green algae, mostly unicellular (though a few form filaments) and with a central constriction dividing the cell into two 'semi-cells'. They are best sampled by taking a handful of submerged *Sphagnum cuspidatum* from within a boggy pool and squeezing the brown humic water into a sample container. As they are relatively large, they can

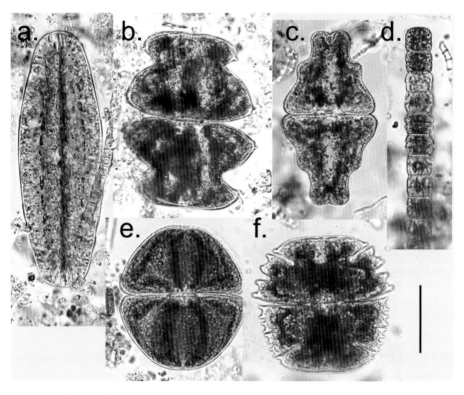

A selection of desmids from a boggy pool beside the Pennine Way in Upper Teesdale: a. *Netrium oblongum*; b. *Micrasterias oscitans (var. mucronata)*; c *Eurastrum didelta*; d. *Desmidium cf. aptogonum*; e. *Cosmarium ralfsii*; f. *Micrasterias truncata.*
© Martyn Kelly

be easily seen and identified using low and medium-power objectives on a compound microscope.

Bryophytes and higher plants

The late Reverend H G Proctor provided one of the best records of the aquatic vegetation prior to flooding (Proctor, 1971). The hard Whin Sill rock at the top of Cauldron Snout formed a low natural dam creating a slow-flowing stretch of the Tees, known as the Weel, which resembled a long, narrow mountain lake, very different from most upland rivers.

This was reflected in the flora, which resembled that of a much lower stretch of river. Proctor's list of plants includes species of *Sparganium*, *Potomageton*, *Myriophyllum*,

Callitriche aquatilis and aquatic *Ranunculus.* He was the first to find the water sedge *(Carex aquatilis)* in the Tees catchment, which was also discovered below Middleton-in-Teesdale by Mrs T Dent. The Weel has unfortunately gone and macrophytes in the reservoir are sparse and almost entirely limited to a few fringing rushes and sedges.

Below Cauldron Snout, however, we find a flora much more typical of an upland river. Here the current is extremely fast and few angiosperms can survive except in sheltered pools at the edge. Those that do occur are found on rocks and boulders and are dominated by aquatic mosses. One bryophyte worthy of particular mention is *Schistidium* (formerly *Grimmia*) *agasizzii.* Until Nigel Holmes found it in the Tees it was known only from Ben Lawers in Scotland. In the Tees it was found to be quite abundant upstream of Middleton, where it was frequently fully submerged in very fast currents (Holmes, 1976).

The effects of Cow Green reservoir can also be seen below the dam. Armitage (1977) noted an increased cover of bryophytes after the dam was closed and Holmes and Whitton (1981) suggested that this was due to a raising of the minimum flow rather than a decrease in the number of floods. Subsequently plant growths have increased still more in some middle stretches of the river.

Invertebrates

The invertebrate fauna of the Upper Tees is dominated by insects, particularly stoneflies *(Plecoptera)* and mayflies *(Ephemoroptera).* 25 of the 35 British stonefly species have been found in the Upper Tees system (Brown, Crag and Crisp, 1964). There have been numerous studies on various insect groups and also on the downstream drift of aquatic invertebrates. Some of the most intensive have been studies of the fauna of the Cow Green reservoir (Armitage, 1978).

An increasing number of trained volunteers is monitoring the health of invertebrate life in the Upper Tees as part of The Riverfly Partnership. This national scheme trains volunteers to gather, sort and record invertebrate samples using a standardised method and set of equipment. The Riverfly Partnership's interest focuses on three key groups of riverflies: the up-wing flies or mayflies *(Ephemeroptera)*, caddisflies or sedges *(Trichoptera)* and stoneflies *(Plecoptera)*. Volunteers collect, identify and count the nymphs and larvae of these groups and the data they collect are used to generate a simple index of the ecological quality of the site. If this index falls to a level that suggests that there may be a problem, the Environment Agency and the Tees Hub Co-Ordinator at the Tees Rivers Trust are both alerted. This results in an investigation which attempts to identify the reason for the alert.

Adult mayfly (missing one tail) near Beckstones Wath bridge near Mickleton © Sara Cox

The Tees Riverfly Partnership volunteers have experienced both the best and the worst. A highlight was the discovery of hundreds of casts from mass-hatchings of large *Plecoptera* in the Greta and watching bullheads ambush and devour unsuspecting olives in the sample tray. Collecting a sample from the Tees at Piercebridge and finding nothing where four weeks earlier there had been a wealth of life was, by contrast, a low point. Both illustrate the rewards and importance of citizen science in helping us to understand and monitor the health of the Tees.

Two of the most spectacular invertebrate species are the white-clawed crayfish *(Austropotomobilis pallipes)* and the

large mayfly *(Ephemera danika)*. The white-clawed crayfish resembles a small lobster and is found in various parts of the Upper Tees and in some of its major tributaries. In recent years its survival in the Tees catchment has been threatened as a result of escapes of the invasive North American signal crayfish *(Pacifastacus leniusculus)*. The signal crayfish is a large, polytrophic crustacean which has invaded waterways across much of Europe (Findlay *et al.*, 2014). This animal is larger and more aggressive than its native cousin and outcompetes it for food and habitat. Additionally, and far more seriously, it carries the crayfish plague, *Aphanomyces astaci*. It is this invasive Oomocyte fungus that has impacted white-clawed crayfish throughout most of the Tees to such an extent that only a few isolated populations of the native species still remain in Upper Teesdale.

The large mayfly is notable both for its large-size and for the synchronised emergence of the adults. In the 1930s Butcher and colleagues found it to be uncommon in the Tees and recorded it only at the lowland site, Eryholme. It now occurs in Cow Green and in the River Lune and in some years large swarms of adults have been seen near Cotherstone.

Left: native white-clawed crayfish (*Austropotomobilis pallipes*) from a survey in Upper Teesdale and, right, a specimen of the introduced signal crayfish (*Pacifastacus leniusculus*).
© Ben Lamb

Fish

The upper Tees is a game fish, rather than a coarse fish, river. Before the days of industrial pollution and abstraction in its lower reaches, it was a major salmon and sea trout river. Between 1904 and 1912 the annual catch by commercial nets was 7,239 salmon and 5,522 sea trout and rod anglers took about 500 salmon and 30 sea trout each year. However industrial developments from about 1920 onwards virtually destroyed the migratory salmonid fishery within a decade.

Following the collapse of the major Teesside industries in the late 1970s and 1980s, the pollution load was reduced and the recovery of salmon and sea trout stocks began. Continued improvements to water quality, particularly in the estuary, brought about by strong regulation from the Environment Agency and its predecessor, the National Rivers Authority, has led to a gradual recovery of the salmon and sea trout stocks, to the extent that juvenile salmon are now abundant and widespread throughout most of the Tees catchment. Despite a relatively low level of angling activity, the annual declared rod catch for salmon has shown a steady rise over the past 20 years.

Some of the upper tributaries, including Egglestone Burn, Bowlees Beck and the rivers Lune and Balder have become established as very important spawning and nursery streams for both salmon and sea trout. However, High Force presents an insurmountable barrier for migratory fish.

Within the upper reaches of the river Tees eel is found as far upstream as High Force, minnow occurs upstream of Cauldron Snout, bullhead occurs well up into the headwaters and brown trout is found throughout almost the entire length of the river. Butcher *et al.* suggested that grayling was introduced to the Tees in about 1880 and in the 1930s its upstream limit was between Piercebridge and Rokeby. However it has increased its range and now occurs at least as far upstream as Middleton-in-Teesdale. Stone loach occurs in the main river at least as far upstream as Middleton, and is also found in the rivers Lune and Balder.

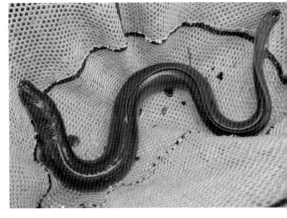

European eel from Scur Beck near Lartington
© Ben Lamb

Perch has been introduced to Hury reservoir and the rainbow trout is an introduction in both Lunedale and Baldersdale reservoirs. Rainbow trout have escaped from the reservoirs and for a short period of time in the late 1990s managed to breed successfully in Carl Beck and some even reverted to the migratory Steelhead form. However, it appears that this population has now disappeared, as juvenile rainbow trout have not been observed for at least the past decade.

The wild brown trout in the upper Tees tend to be small, typically about 100 g each, though a few larger fish are caught each year. Since the construction of Cow Green reservoir, fish in the reservoir have grown rapidly and specimens of over 1.8 kg were taken in the early years after impoundment.

Invasive Non Native Species

Invasive Non Native Species (INNS) pose an enormous threat to global biodiversity. Waterways are particularly susceptible to INNS. Aside from the signal crayfish (above) a number of highly invasive plant and animal species are already present in the upper Tees, both in the water itself as well as on the riverbanks. Himalayan balsam *(Impatiens glandulifera)*, Japanese knotweed *(Falopia japonica)* and giant hogweed *(Heracleum mantegazzianum)* are present and the Tees Rivers Trust is co-ordinating efforts to control them. However, there are other species that pose a great threat to the ecology of the river. Of particular note are salmon fluke *(Gyrodactylus salaris)* and killer shrimp *(Dikerogammarus haemobaphes)*. The Tees biosecurity plan (2014) sets out measures to avoid their introduction as well as actions to contain them and ensure their swift eradication.

Visitors to Upper Teesdale should be aware of the risk of both importing and exporting invasive species. It is important that clothing and equipment, in particular walking shoes, canoes and angling gear, is checked for any foreign matter, cleaned and dried.

How have the reservoirs influenced aquatic life in Upper Teesdale?

In addition to altering the flow regime (see above), Cow Green and the other reservoirs of Upper Teesdale have had a number of other effects on the biology of the Tees and her tributaries. Impounding a huge quantity of water in one of the coolest parts of the country also affects the temperature of the river, due to water's high specific heat capacity. This means that there is not just a narrower range of flows, but also a narrower range of temperature recorded. The difference between coolest and warmest temperatures in the Tees below Cow Green dropped by $1 - 2$ °C, which may not seem a lot, but one consequence is to delay the warming of the river water in Spring by about a month which, in turn, delays the development of young trout. However, Crisp *et al.* (1983) went on to show that any reduction in growth rate due to lower temperatures was actually offset by other side-effects of the dam (such as a less harsh flow regime) to result in an increase in the total density of fish downstream. Patrick Armitage (2006) has shown significant shifts in the types of invertebrate found in the Tees below Cow Green, with a decrease in taxa that are adapted to a harsh hydrological regime, as might be expected. Maize Beck, a tributary which joins just below Cauldron Snout, and which has a natural flow regime, shows many fewer changes over the same time period.

The reservoirs also have major effects on the movement of gravel by the river. Gravels provide habitat for phytobenthos and invertebrates, a growing medium for macrophytes and spawning medium and juvenile habitat for fish and fry. They also have a great influence on the geomorphology of the river, forming pools, riffles, banksides and bars.

Brook lamprey *(Lampetra planeri)*, a species found in local becks such as Wilden Beck near Cotherstone
© E J Langton-Airey

The presence of several reservoirs in Upper Teesdale has had a significant impact both on the mobility of gravels through the system as well as on the flow that provides the energy to move, form, deposit and erode gravel from flood plains and banksides. Rayner and Girvan (2010) estimate that the impoundments on the Balder and Lune systems have collectively reduced salmonid spawning habitat potential by 900,000 eggs. They also note the loss of spawning downstream due to lack of replenishment. Work to augment gravel in the Balder was carried out below Hury Reservoir in 2007 by the Environment Agency and again in 2012 by the Tees Rivers Trust.

References

Armitage, P D (1977), Invertebrate drift in the regulated River Tees and an unregulated tributary, Maize Beck, below Cow Green dam. *Freshwater Biology* **7**: 167-183.

Armitage, P D (2006), Long-term faunal changes in a regulated and an unregulated stream – Cow Green thirty years on, *River Research and Applications* **22**: 957-966.

Atkinson, K (1998), 'The initial development of net phytoplankton in Cow Green reservoir (Upper Teesdale): a new impoundment in Northern England', pp 30-43, in Round F E (ed.), *Algae and the Aquatic Environment*, Biopress, Bristol.

Brown, V M, Cragg, J B & Crisp, D T (1964), The Plecoptera of the Moor House National Nature Reserve, Westmorland. *Transactions of the Society for British Entomology* **16**: 123-134.

Butcher, R W, Longwell, J & Pentelow, F T K (1937), *Survey of the River Tees, Pt III*, Water Pollution Research Technical Paper N° 6, HMSO.

Crisp, D T (1977), Some physical and chemical effects of the Cow Green (Upper Teesdale) impoundment. *Freshwater Biology* **7**: 109-120.

Crisp, D T, Mann, R H K & Cubby, P R (1983), Effects of regulation on the River Tees upon fish populations below Cow Green Reservoir, *Journal of Applied Ecology* **20**: 371-386.

Findlay, J D S, Riley, W D & Lucas, M C (2014), 'Signal crayfish (Pacifastacus leniusculus) predation upon Atlantic salmon (Salmo salar) eggs.', *Aquatic conservation : marine and freshwater ecosystems*, **25**: 250-258.

Rayner, S and Girvan, J (2010), Tees Reservoir Flows and Gravel Project, Pre-Feasibility Report, Report to the Environment Agency, Royal Haskoning, Newcastle.

Holmes, N T H (1976), The distribution and ecology of *Grimmia agassizii* (Sull. & Lesq.) in Teesdale. *Journal of Bryology* **9**: 275-278.

Holmes, N T H & Whitton, B A (1981), Phytobenthos of the River Tees and its tributaries, *Freshwater Biology* **11**: 139-168.

Kelly, M G (2006), 'A comparison of diatoms with other phytobenthos as indicators of ecological status in streams in northern England, 139-151', Proceedings of the 18th International Diatom Symposium (edited by A Witkowski), Biopress, Bristol.

Livingstone, D & Whitton, B A (1984), Water chemistry and phosphatase activity of the blue-green alga Rivularia in Upper Teesdale streams, *Journal of Ecology* **72**: 405-421.

Proctor, H G (1971), Aquatic macrophytes of the Weel of the Tees, *The Vasculum* **56**: 59-66.

Chapter 9

Conservation

Stephen Trotter

Introduction

As previous chapters testify, this northern Pennine dale is by almost any measure a very special place. Upper Teesdale is amongst the most remote and relatively unspoilt places in England and has long been recognised as having some very special geological features, archaeological remains, unique habitats and celebrated wildlife. The most celebrated rare habitats and their suite of famous species largely persist as post-glacial survivals on the unique sugar limestone, rocky outcrops and limestone flushes. The Dale continues to be a tourist attraction and to excite scientific research, while providing a livelihood and home to thousands of people.

A plethora of conservation measures, particularly related to wildlife, has been applied over recent decades with some, but not universal, success. Conservation

significance has always been high but in recent years its value and importance have grown even more against the wider context of the continuing trends of biodiversity decline almost everywhere else in the English Uplands.

The only exceptions to this slow decline seem to be uplands where there has been a vision to restore habitats and species through recovery programmes. Where more sustainable methods have been implemented by farmers, landowners and land managers using their own resources and with help from agri-environment schemes, Non Government Organisations (NGOs), some local authorities and occasionally funds from water companies, the trends of decline have been successfully reversed. Where resource and resolve have been applied, geological and archaeological conservation has also been successful.

What is so significant?

The drone's aerial view above shows how small the grasslands are that hold the rich and unusual Teesdale specialities, compared to the surrounding extensive hills, in-bye and moorlands. These tiny grassland 'jewels' sit scattered across the landscape like small islands within an 'ocean' of relatively common, widely distributed moorland and farmland habitats.

The whole landscape deserves protection and the 'jewels' merit the highest conservation efforts because they are so rare and unusual. Their intrinsic interest defines them as invaluable national and international priorities. Unfavourable change, historic and current, in many other uplands has continued a fall in abundance and numbers of species present (State of Nature report 2016). But in Upper Teesdale many of these typical and once-common upland species are still reasonably abundant.

A drone's aerial view looking south over Cronkley Fell
© Martin Townsend (Valley Drone)

Exceptional herb-rich meadow, the Tattyfield, Baldersdale
© John O'Reilly

In recent decades, there has been a growing recognition of the increasing national significance and value of the whole Teesdale landscape. Two important examples demonstrate the point — the survival of species-rich upland hay meadows and the assemblage of upland breeding waders and other birds like black grouse. Upper Teesdale is exceptional and increasingly distinctive for both, in terms of the habitats and species present, and the abundance at which they occur.

The conservation significance of Upper Teesdale lies in the:

• unique habitats and good populations of nationally rare species which sit at the interface between northern and southern populations, with a high representation of arctic and arctic-alpine elements;

• scale, quality and character of its semi-natural habitats and the intimate mosaic of rich and diverse habitats;

• assemblages / populations of upland birds and invertebrates that were once common across the uplands, especially on enclosed in-bye, but which have seen major declines elsewhere since 1970;

• special landforms, spectacular waterfalls, rivers and rugged beauty that varies over the seasons;

• relative intactness of the landscape which hasn't been fragmented to any great extent by land use change or development (with the obvious exception of Cow Green reservoir). Upper Teesdale is also intimately connected with the Pennine chain to the north, south and west which is of significant benefit to those species which rely upon the exchange of individuals between different populations. This should also be an important benefit for species as they begin to adapt to a changing climate as they can migrate towards the north and west; and

- heritage — how people have gleaned a living from these hills for 8,000 years with many successive generations leaving their mark. The more recent legacy of lead mining, quarrying and farming, and understanding the deep landscape history of how the area functions and has developed in the way it has, with local dialect, pride and resilience.

As a long devotee of the Pennines in general, my first visit to Upper Teesdale on a witheringly cold April day in 1980 won my heart for the rest of my life. I trudged up the Cow Green road — across what seemed an endless moorland of yellow mat-grass; bleak and apparently lifeless after a long winter and which is so typical of the Pennines and a legacy of sheep grazing. I will never forget my first sight of the electrifying blue of a spring gentian — the brilliant blue that no photograph or drawing can ever capture. Words fail to express the joy and delight of the tiny bright pins in the grass. How could such unfeasibly delicate and stunning flowers survive up here in this desolate place — dazzling and contrasting so incongruously against the drab moorland?

Choose your way, long or short
© Anne Kelly

Visitors are not new and come for different reasons. Some pass through quickly in cars and on bikes, others cycling, walking the Pennine Way or taking more leisurely paths. Day visits are common but local hotels and other accommodation types are particularly busy in the warmer months. The Dale is a big attraction for outdoor pursuits, especially canoeing at Low Force. Visitors bring welcome cash to boost the local economy. But large numbers at popular sites can put pressure on sensitive habitats and species.

Locals can tell a similar compelling story of wonder and awe of the Dale from a different, year-round perspective that mixes harsh winters as well as pleasant sunny days. Visitors should recognise and appreciate that the Dale is as it is largely because of the people who live, work and learn here.

So we should conserve Upper Teesdale for two reasons, for:

- its own sake and its intrinsic interest; and
- what it provides for society — a home and livelihood, food, tourism, carbon, biodiversity, clean water and air.

How is nature faring in Upper Teesdale?

Whilst there has been some change and decline in the quality of some habitats and the abundance of species present, the rate and extent of decline has been far less in Upper Teesdale. For a variety of reasons, the conservation status has remained relatively good — but it could be better.

Since the loss of 8.4 ha (21 acres) of species-rich calcareous grassland and base-rich flushes by the flooding of Cow Green reservoir in 1972, there has been little reported major reduction in the extent of key habitats in Upper Teesdale. However, this overall picture of successful protection masks the ongoing deterioration in quality of many of the Dale's most important and precious habitats and a decline in the populations of some key species.

River Tees flowing from the Cow Green dam outlet
© Anne Kelly

One of the issues facing nature conservation is the absence of records and the memory of how diverse and rich places used to be. We are not good at tracking or recognising the slow and creeping deterioration of habitat quality that may result from subtle changes in management — changes may take decades and we rarely monitor at a level of detail to detect them. Those of us who have only known Teesdale in close detail since the late 1990s are rightly under the impression that this is a superb area for its natural history. It is, but we have no personal knowledge of what was there before, how the landscape has changed and what has been lost.

Those with that memory provide powerful witness to some subtle changes in the Dale. (Bradshaw, M E, 2012), for example, reports that following decades of satisfactory management in the mid-twentieth century, there has been 'an insidious reduction in the size of the populations of most of the rare plant species, accompanied by a deterioration in the quality of many of the plant communities'.

This is supported by her outstanding long-term monitoring study of the populations of initially 18 and latterly six key species. Large decreases in the populations of these six plants were observed between 1975 and 2002 — especially on Widdybank and Cronkley Fells.

Much of the deterioration seems to be linked to variations in the numbers and type of grazing animals — particularly fluctuations in sheep, cattle and rabbit grazing. Overgrazing causes direct damage to the sward and reductions in the rarities. Undergrazing, on the other hand, produces a tall, close sward which leads to many of the rarities being shaded out — again leading to a reduction in their populations. The extent of the problem means that any full recovery to the population levels of the mid-twentieth century may need further intervention. Elsewhere, such as at Cetry Bank, changes in livestock timing and type has resulted damage to the vegetation.

The key problem is how to ensure the right level of grazing across a mosaic of grassland types each with slightly different requirements — that will allow the majority of rare species to recover their populations.

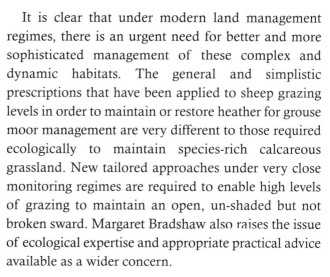

It is clear that under modern land management regimes, there is an urgent need for better and more sophisticated management of these complex and dynamic habitats. The general and simplistic prescriptions that have been applied to sheep grazing levels in order to maintain or restore heather for grouse moor management are very different to those required ecologically to maintain species-rich calcareous grassland. New tailored approaches under very close monitoring regimes are required to enable high levels of grazing to maintain an open, un-shaded but not broken sward. Margaret Bradshaw also raises the issue of ecological expertise and appropriate practical advice available as a wider concern.

Blue moor-grass can shade out rarer species. Mowing is only a short-term solution © Margaret E Bradshaw

The immediate effect of release from grazing was also observed as an outcome of the foot and mouth outbreak in 2001 (Roberts, 2003). In general the sheep reduction benefitted the shrubs of open moorland — and initially resulted in the abundant flowering of rare plants in pockets of calcareous grassland within the moorland. However, the longer-term reduction in grazing that followed, resulted in a taller sward — raising concerns that many of the rarities may be shaded-out and/or out-competed. As the ranker grasses accumulate litter and biomass, they become less attractive as food to grazing animals and the problems for small herbs are compounded.

Inevitably, Upper Teesdale is subject to many of the same pressures and trends that have affected land management in other parts of the English Uplands. The impacts of historic grazing take a considerable length of time to reverse. The number of sheep in many areas has been reduced but the impacts of decades of high levels of grazing will take years to reverse and in some circumstances may require intervention to restore their condition. Some of the pressure on out-bye has been transferred to in-bye areas where there are some issues of soil compaction and change in pasture management. In some areas there has been a general decline in levels of rush management and this could affect the use of in-bye land by waders.

One of the most worrying and as yet unexplained trends is for the continuing decline in quality of hay meadows. This seems to have occurred even in some of the best meadows where management has been closely monitored and yet some of the more sensitive hay meadow species have been lost — even though no obvious management changes have taken place. Further research into these declines is required but they may be linked to subtle change in timings of key operations, weather or nutrient inputs (eg. from atmospheric deposition).

Few assessments have been made into the use of wormers and other pesticides in upland areas, and their impacts on invertebrates in soil and freshwater systems.

There has been concern amongst conservationists about the creeping slow intensification even on farms within agri-environment schemes. Natural England has been criticised for its apparent lack of action in tackling some of the issues.

The recent State of Nature Report (2016) indicated the continuing loss of biodiversity in the uplands with 56% of species in decline and others increasing. The key problem is that many species which might be considered as specialists are under pressure — whilst generalist species that can adapt to changing environments are increasing in abundance.

According to the most recently available data (mostly from 2010 and 2012), most of the SSSI habitats in Upper Teesdale are not in favourable condition for nature conservation and could be better. Only 12.26%

Peat restoration — taking a plug of peat to block a grip © North Pennines AONB Partnership

of the area is in good condition — an area of 1,760 ha. The vast majority, 85.69% is judged as being unfavourable recovering. This means that there is a positive management plan, entry into an agri-environment scheme and /or work programme planned across 12.309 ha which is thought will lead to recovery in time. Around 2% is classed as being in unfavourable condition with no change.

The reasons for these failures are varied but usually relate to historic over- or under-grazing, peat erosion, poaching (damage by stock trampling), negative indicators, for example too few key species for different reasons, too many rushes.

What does conservation mean here?

Although distinctive even amongst Pennine dales, Upper Teesdale shares a common suite of upland species and habitats with the hills to the north and south. It has a broad range of ecosystem services and attributes in common, similar landscape character, a similar set of upland agricultural and land management issues — and the Teesdale economy and community has a great deal in common with other upland areas.

Upper Teesdale has eleven environmental 'designations' (Natural England, December 2017). The most important of these designations, in terms of geological, habitat and species protection, is the network of Sites of Special Scientific Interest (under UK legislation) and Special Protection Areas for birds / Special Areas of Conservation (European Union Directives which apply the Bern Convention, 1979 into

EU and UK law). Archaeological sites are protected by Historic England.

Designations help, but we must be reminded that conservation isn't just a scientific exercise and it isn't just about legislative protection, or about rules and regulations that are often seen as being inflexible, much to the frustration of farmers and landowners.

So far, a suite of inter-related factors has helped conservation in the Dale:

Continuity of approach to land management

The role of landowners, land managers and farmers is crucial. Some modern techniques and technology have been applied to increase productivity (such as silage, larger machinery, use of quad bikes, modern chemical treatments) but an otherwise more-or-less traditional approach to farming is practised, probably because there are few cost-effective alternatives.

In essence, there is a high proportion of farms which are still run as nature-friendly farms, under what has become known as High Nature Value Farming systems, whether intentionally or not.

Traditional hill farming is crucial for conservation
© Anne Kelly

The reformed Common Agricultural Policy has helped sustain these systems through Higher Level Stewardship (the so-called agri-environment schemes) which reward farming that is 'environmentally-friendly'. Payments are made that recognise the costs (or income foregone) of looking after or enhancing some habitats. This public investment has kept farmers farming and sustained many wild flower-rich hay meadows, restored wetlands, planted hedges, rebuilt walls (though not really critical for nature conservation), improved peat bogs and paid for reductions in grazing levels on some sensitive areas.

Pattern of land ownership

The majority of land ownership falls within two large estates (and the Ministry of Defence), which I would argue has had a positive overall impact for nature conservation because they can bring a long-term perspective and continuity of objectives to land management, even if there are outstanding differences of opinion about management.

Remoteness, climate and less favourable environment for farming

It has always been more difficult to introduce more intensive land-use techniques which have been to the detriment of wildlife in other places.

Designations and rules

There is no doubt that the various pieces of legislation (especially the Wildlife and Countryside Act, 1981, the Birds and Habitats Directives and the Natural Environment and Rural Communities Act, 2005, CAP cross-compliance) have played an important and critical role in protecting the wildlife value of Upper Teesdale. Designation of extensive areas as Sites of Special Scientific Interest and as the Moor House–Upper Teesdale National Nature Reserve have played a vital role in sustaining much of the biodiversity interest — even though there are ongoing and frequent disagreements with Natural England and NGOs about the details of what the best management should be. The work and considerable efforts of the North Pennines AONB staff unit, National Nature Reserve staff and Natural England conservation staff is also recognised as having played a vital part in keeping Upper Teesdale special.

The designation of the North Pennines as an Area of Outstanding Natural Beauty (NPAONB) in 1988 has also been a very significant factor in the conservation

Welcome to Moor House—Upper Teesdale NNR
© Steve Gater

of Upper Teesdale — and will continue to be so into the future. The exemplary approach and positive programme of activity (for example on peatland restoration, hay meadows, tourism, education and promotion of better understanding, partnership projects, creation of the UNESCO Global Geopark) of the NPAONB unit has delivered some important programmes and conservation outcomes — and will have a key role in future implementation of policy.

Control of predators
While there are uncertainties and wider controversies about the impact of game management on the environment and wild species, for example, in respect of the impact of releasing large numbers of pheasants — and grouse moor management (such as the impact of heather burning on peat and the illegal persecution of protected species), recent scientific evidence indicates that populations of ground-nesting birds benefit from the legal control of predators such as foxes, crows and mustelids. Illegal persecution of other predators in uplands is a nation-wide problem that cannot be condoned and ways need to be found to secure the conservation of the species targeted.

Farm payments
The Common Agricultural Policy (CAP) has played a key role in enabling farming and nature-friendly farming to continue in the Dale in recent decades. Essentially, in terms of food production, traditional UK hill farming is not financially competitive because of its inherent environmental and structural disadvantages, and its high costs, compared with the lowlands or farming systems elsewhere. Hill farm incomes are very low and nationally the majority of businesses depend on the tax payer with around 80% of hill farming income coming from subsidy payments (for example area payments —

Basic Payment; and agri-environment payments through Higher Level Stewardship). The average age of hill farmers in England is around 60 to 70 and low incomes mean that fewer young people may wish to follow their parents into hill farming. Without payment mechanisms to keep hill farmers farming in a nature-friendly way, then many, if not all, will disappear if they cannot diversify, with potentially disastrous consequences for habitats and wildlife that require active management for their maintenance, let alone restoration.

Ongoing conservation

Natural England and the North Pennines AONB (NPAONB) are key players in making conservation happen. As the NPAONB Management Plan states: 'Decline in upland biodiversity must be reversed, which will be achieved through the conservation, enhancement, expansion and connection of protected habitats and communities of wildlife'. The Wildlife Trusts, and other organisations, also have an important role to play.

Any conservation strategy, if it is to be successful, must be embedded in the economic and social fabric of the local community. People are important and the social, economic and cultural vitality of Teesdale is as much part of the equation as its wildlife — they are interdependent.

It is vital for the future of the wildlife of Upper Teesdale that farmers and landowners are motivated, committed and properly rewarded for caring for the natural environment and natural heritage of the Dale. They must have a stake in conservation and they hold the future in their hands. Public policy must ensure that creating a healthy living landscape, full of wildlife, must and will provide local people with a viable and good living — either directly or as the basis of other products and/or services that are needed by wider society

Future public policy should provide mechanisms to ensure that Upper Teesdale's precious natural environment is loved, understood, well managed and improved by present and future generations of local people. It must work with the factors identified above — and drive the delivery of the things that society needs and wants. Upper Teesdale not only has intrinsic value in itself, but it also provides things for people and society, including:

- a home and place of work for people of all ages;
- high quality, nutritious and sustainably-produced local food;
- lots of wildlife — high biodiversity;
- clean unpolluted water catchments where it costs less to treat drinking water and doesn't damage the environment downstream;
- clean unpolluted air that supports sensitive species including rare lichens and algae;
- healthy soils that capture more carbon as organic matter, hold back the flow to reduce flooding risks downstream, are naturally fertile and are more resilient to drought;
- places to walk and relax, boosting health and wellbeing;
- a place that people want to visit and stay time and again, supporting a thriving tourist economy; and
- landscapes that are resilient to climate change and future extreme weather events.

Society must continue to step in — where the market fails to deliver these things — by investing in positive mechanisms that support sustainable land management and renewable environmental assets. Winning the hearts and minds of farmers, landowners and land managers is vital, and ensuring there is a strong and clear financial interest for everyone in wildlife and natural beauty is essential.

At times, we will also need to remind society of the importance and relevance of Upper Teesdale to everyone's lives, whether they live in Middleton, Middlesbrough or Manchester.

Ultimately our lives depend on a healthy natural environment, and Upper Teesdale is an irreplaceable national asset — as important and precious to the nation's heritage as any Constable painting or repairs to the Houses of Parliament or Westminster Abbey, the Royal Opera House or the Lindisfarne Gospels.

One of the most important conservation insights that have been gained in recent decades is that traditional conservation activities cannot on their own hold back the process of change; at best they can slow its rate and/or influence its outcomes. We can't put a fence round it and leave it alone. Change in the natural environment is inevitable and ubiquitous; and rather than fight it, if conservation is to be successful, it must work to manage and influence the process and direction of change so that species and habitats can adapt and thrive. We must also recognise that environmental, sociological, technological and economic changes driven by human activity and wider society far beyond the immediate geography of Upper Teesdale, are also fundamentally affecting the wildlife and future of the attributes that we value and cherish.

So conservation should embrace the process of change; but it must lead and manage the direction of change so that the important features of significance that we value, and the processes on which they depend, are safeguarded and transferred from the present to the future. The key objective is therefore to manage the Dale in a way that secures biodiversity, helping species and habitats adapt to change in the best possible way — and to ensure that we take as much as possible of what makes Upper Teesdale special into the future.

This is a complex and difficult task in a rapidly changing, uncertain and unpredictable world as the UK leaves the European Union. It is impossible to separate the fate of the ecosystem from the wider social and economic factors of the 'human ecology' in Upper Teesdale. The future of Upper Teesdale's wildlife is intimately linked to the future of its people — and their view of whether the wildlife is important to them and their livelihoods.

In the twentieth century, a great deal of time and energy were spent in creating nature reserves and designating sites. That was really important and as with the Upper Teesdale experience of designation, we would certainly have lost far more biodiversity than has occurred without this approach.

But the process of designating places doesn't ensure the survival of their species and habitats — species don't recognise boundaries and many sites even in large areas like the key habitats of Upper Teesdale need to be connected to those around the Dale — especially along the Pennine chain so that species can move. Given that all of the significant species and habitats in Upper Teesdale require open and grazed landscapes, as opposed to shaded and wooded habitats, some form of management interventions are critical for nature conservation.t

Some change we can influence or prevent, other drivers of change, we can't. The process of conservation as an activity is therefore

Harvesting hay meadow seed for restoration work through the AONB Partnership's Nectarworks project
© Ruth Starr-Keddle, North Pennines AONB Partnership

about how we manage the impact of anticipated change on the species, habitats and natural processes that we value and cherish. It's about choosing the attributes of the natural history of Teesdale that we want to pass to future generations so that they too can enjoy and be inspired.

Probably of greatest relevance to future conservation in Upper Teesdale is finding mechanisms to enable nature-friendly farming systems to thrive and become profitable as we leave the European Union. Nature-friendly farming systems (also known as High Nature Value Farming) are low-intensity farming systems that are particularly valuable for wildlife, the environment and people. Low intensity does not mean low maintenance! Looking after livestock, farmland birds and meadows is a time-consuming, labour intensive and expensive business which requires great skill and knowledge.

A great deal depends on government policy and future payment schemes and although there is at present great uncertainty, the 25 Year Plan for the Environment indicates the direction of travel may well be favourable for special places like Upper Teesdale.

The key is recognition that farmers are not currently paid for all of the things they produce for society — and they should be. Farmer support networks are also critical and farmers working together can find solutions to our environmental solutions, if they're given clear outcomes to deliver and the freedom to work out how to achieve them without being micro-managed. Major change is on the way and it's really important that we help both wildlife and local people to adapt to the new world. Part of the solution is ensuring that society makes the right payments for the right things but it's also about how distinctive areas like Upper Teesdale can produce high quality local food for local markets

Merlin
© Hilary Chambers

Hypogymnia physodes, a lichen
© Lesley Hodgson

— and pasture-fed beef and lamb has been shown to attract a premium whilst producing healthier food and environmental benefits.

A vision for the future

It is important that a vision is urgently agreed for the conservation of Upper Teesdale at a whole landscape-scale. The vision must be shared and adopted in a partnership by as many of those people and organisations who can make it a reality — and share an interest in the future. It is important that this is tailored to local needs and is 'bottom-up', respecting the different roles and expertise that different individuals and groups can bring.

Globeflower
© Anne Kelly

The economic value of tourism to the Dale should not be forgotten. Spectacular landscape, wildlife and opportunity for a variety of country pursuits will continue to encourage people to visit. Local folk need to earn a living to ensure that it continues to be such a treasured place. There are controversial management issues that need to be addressed to find solutions that satisfy the interests of different parties. When there is strong understanding and agreement on an inclusive vision, the key issues and problems can be defined as part of developing the strategy and action plan.

Conservation policy and public investment in Upper Teesdale, in partnership with local people, should deliver the following vision;

• a living landscape where the special open habitats of Upper Teesdale are wilder and better than they are at the moment — with more wildlife and without losing any of the key species as a result of illegal, inappropriate or inadequate management. There will be an integrated ecosystems-based plan for more

Melancholy thistle
© Steve Gater

habitat, better managed habitat, bigger core areas of habitat in the right places which are well connected and integrated with the surrounding landscape;

- restored and safeguarded degraded habitats, especially blanket peat, hay meadows and key grassland areas;
- enhanced opportunities for people to connect first hand with relatively wild nature in high quality habitats;
- people recognised as a fundamental part of the upland ecosystem where nature-friendly / high nature value farming is standard. Farmers and land managers are rewarded properly for the valuable and multiple things they produce for society (but for which they currently don't get paid) via contracts with the state and a reformed land management payments system. Farmers and land managers are encouraged to work together to find and implement practical economic solutions to achieve the wildlife and environmental outcomes that society wants; and
- people, whether local or visitors, are valued and welcomed more as an integral part of the upland scene in Teesdale.

Conclusion

If restored, Upper Teesdale could be an even better and more wildlife-rich landscape at the heart of the Pennines. With sufficient investment of time, effort, emotional energy and hard cash, land management could provide current and future generations with greater economic prosperity and make an even bigger contribution to the health and wellbeing of society — to those who live there, in the surrounding lowlands and those who visit.

That will only succeed if there is a sensible vision

that hill farmers and landowners support and their children buy into. Government policy is critical and must recognise the full value of Upper Teesdale's importance in decision-making and spatial planning — this really is a special case.

Policy incentives and subsidies should be aligned and consistent. Public payments should incentivise farmers and landowners to provide multiple benefits for society. The principle of 'public payments for public benefit' is applied to provide a fair mechanism for addressing market failures in environmental management.

New economic models should be developed, for example, in natural capital maintenance payments, offsetting and other innovative ways of adding economic returns from High Nature Value Farming. A new generation of hill farmers will need to be attracted to this approach because it gives more business opportunities and it makes financial and business sense. Farmers should have a stake in sustaining wildlife-rich farming systems and receive full financial reward from society for the benefits they deliver.

The restoration of habitats and more natural processes in Upper Teesdale will increase resilience and adaptation to the uncertainties and extremes of a changing climate. Restored and natural peat bogs will retain their carbon stores and help to fix and lock-up more atmospheric carbon as well as becoming more wildlife-rich.

References and further reading

Bradshaw, M E, 2012, British Wildlife, vol.23:6, 'The Upper Teesdale Assemblage of rare plants in decline'.

Rawlins, J, An 1844 Pennine Way from Tees to Ribble, 2016

Roberts, J, North Pennines News Spring & Summer 2009

Rudd, M, The discovery of Teesdale, 2007

State of Nature 2016, report by 25 nature conservation organisations, September 2016.

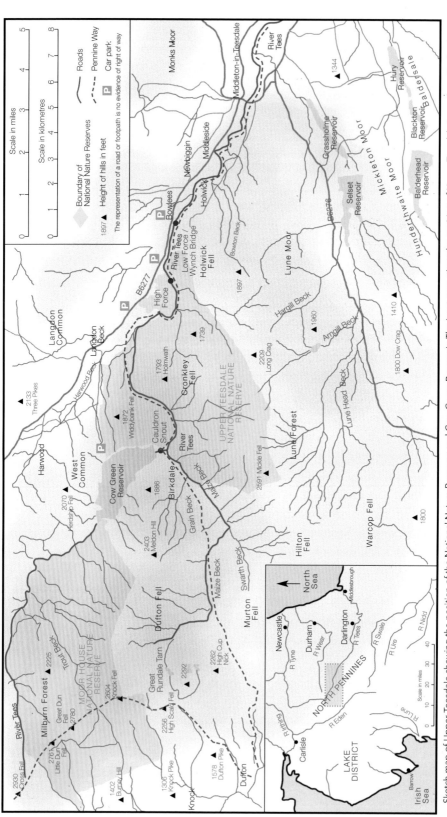

Sketch map of Upper Teesdale showing the position of the National Nature Reserves and Cow Green Reservoir. The inset map gives the position of Upper Teesdale in northern England.

© Dr G A L Johnson (deceased), Mrs D Wilson and Mosaic Print & Design.

The essential map for outdoor activities is Ordnance Survey Explorer map OL31.